Everyday Mathematics®

The University of Chicago School Mathematics Project

Assessment Handbook

Grade 2

McGraw Hill Education

Chicago, IL • Columbus, OH • New York, NY

The University of Chicago School Mathematics Project (UCSMP)

Max Bell, Director, UCSMP Elementary Materials Component; Director, *Everyday Mathematics* First Edition
James McBride, Director, *Everyday Mathematics* Second Edition
Andy Isaacs, Director, *Everyday Mathematics* Third Edition
Amy Dillard, Associate Director, *Everyday Mathematics* Third Edition
Rachel Malpass McCall, Associate Director, *Everyday Mathematics* Common Core State Standards Edition

Authors
Jean Bell, William M. Carroll, Amy Dillard, Kathleen Pitvorec

Common Core State Standards Edition
Sarah R. Burns, Mary Ellen Dairyko, Rachel Malpass McCall, Cheryl G. Moran, Lila K. Schwartz

Teacher in Residence
Soundarya Radhakrishnan

Technical Art
Diana Barrie

Contributors
Linda Aponte, Megan Donovan, Syeda Sayeed, Mary Eileen Weber; Sharon Draznin, Nancy Hanvey, Laurie Leff, Denise Porter, Herb Price, Joyce Timmons, Lisa Winters

Acknowledgements
We gratefully acknowledge the work of the following classroom teachers who provided input and suggestions as we designed this handbook: Huong Banh, Fran Moore, Jenny Waters, and Lana Winnet.

Photo Credits
Cover (l)Linda Lewis/Frank Lane Picture Agency/CORBIS, (r)C Squared Studios/Getty Images, (bkgd)Estelle Klawitter/Cusp/CORBIS; **Back Cover Spine** C Squared Studios/Getty Images; **others** The McGraw-Hill Companies.

Permissions
The quotes on pages 4, 5, 8, and 35 are reprinted with permission from *Knowing What Students Know: The Science and Design of Educational Assessment* © 2001 by the National Academy of Sciences, courtesy of the National Academies Press, Washington, D.C.

everyday**math**.com

Education

Send all inquiries to:
McGraw-Hill Education
STEM Learning Solutions Center
P.O. Box 812960
Chicago, IL 60681

ISBN: 978-0-07-657700-2
MHID: 0-07-657700-7

Printed in the United States of America.

1 2 3 4 5 6 7 8 9 QDB 17 16 15 14 13 12 11

McGraw-Hill is committed to providing instructional materials in Science, Technology, Engineering, and Mathematics (STEM) that give all students a solid foundation, one that prepares them for college and careers in the 21st century.

The **McGraw·Hill** Companies

Contents

Philosophy of Assessment in *Everyday Mathematics*®

Introduction

Too often, school assessment tends to provide only scattered snapshots of student achievement rather than continuous records of growth. In *Everyday Mathematics,* assessment is like a motion picture, revealing the development of each child's mathematical understanding over time while also giving the teacher useful feedback about the instructional needs of individual children and the class.

For assessment to be useful to teachers, children, parents, and others, the *Everyday Mathematics* authors believe that...

◆ Teachers need to have a variety of assessment tools and techniques to choose from so children can demonstrate what they know in a variety of ways and teachers can have reliable information from multiple sources.

◆ Children should be included in the assessment process. Self assessment and reflection are skills children will develop over time if they are encouraged.

◆ Assessment and instruction should be closely aligned. Assessment should assist teachers in making instructional decisions concerning individual children and the class.

◆ Assessment should focus on all important outcomes, not only on outcomes that are easy to measure.

◆ A good assessment program makes instruction easier.

◆ The best assessment plans are developed by teachers working collaboratively within their schools and districts.

Everyday Mathematics offers many opportunities for assessing children's knowledge and skills. This handbook describes the *Everyday Mathematics* assessment resources and serves as a guide for navigating through those resources and helping you design and implement a balanced classroom assessment plan.

Balanced Assessment

When planning a balanced assessment, begin by asking several basic questions:

- *What are the purposes of assessment?*
- *What are the contexts for assessment?*
- *What are the sources of evidence for assessment?*
- *What content is assessed?*

What Are the Purposes of Assessment?

The purposes of assessment serve three main functions: to support learning, to measure achievement, and to evaluate programs. Each purpose is integral to achieving a balanced assessment plan.

Formative assessment supports learning by providing information about children's current knowledge and abilities so you can plan future instruction more effectively. Formative assessment encourages children to identify their areas of weakness or strength so they can focus their efforts more precisely.

Summative assessment measures student growth and achievement. A summative assessment might be designed, for example, to determine whether children have learned certain material by the end of a fixed period of study.

Program evaluation means judging how well a program is working. A school district, for example, may want to identify schools with especially strong mathematics programs so their successes can be replicated in other schools with weaker programs. Program evaluation makes this possible.

Assessment tools and techniques often serve more than one purpose. Assessments built into a curriculum might give teachers information they can use to plan future instruction more effectively or prepare progress reports. District administrators might use this information to allocate professional development resources.

Purposes of Assessment

Formative Assessment	Summative Assessment	Program Evaluation
◆ Used to plan instruction ◆ Helps students to reflect on their progress	◆ Used to measure student growth and achievement ◆ Helps determine if students have learned content	◆ Used to evaluate overall success of the math program

What Are the Contexts for Assessment?

Assessment occurs in a variety of contexts.

◆ **Ongoing assessment** involves gathering information from children's everyday work. These assessments can take place at the same time as regular classroom instruction.

◆ **Periodic assessment** consists of formal assessments that are built in to a curriculum, such as an end-of-unit Progress Check.

◆ **External assessment** is independent of the curriculum. An example of an external assessment is a standardized test.

Everyday Mathematics supports all three contexts for assessment, and it provides tools and materials for ongoing and periodic assessments that you can use to create a balanced assessment plan.

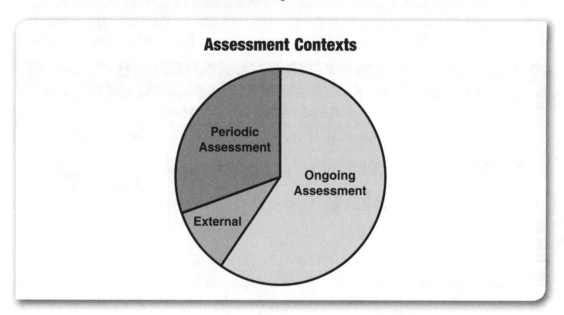

The sizes of the sections of the circle in the figure above are meant to be suggestive, but the exact proportions of ongoing, periodic, and external assessments will vary depending on your grade level, the time of year, state and district mandates, and many other factors.

For all *Everyday Mathematics* assessments, provide children with tools that may be helpful in completing the assessment. Such tools include, but are not limited to, number lines, number grids, scratch paper, base-10 blocks, coins and bills, counters, blank situation diagrams, Pattern Blocks, and Pattern-Block Templates.

What Are the Sources of Evidence for Assessment?

> *Assessment is a process of reasoning from evidence.*
>
> (Pellegrino, Chudowsky, and Glaser 2001, 36)

The evidence for assessing what children know is indirect because we cannot know exactly what they are thinking. Evidence about children's knowledge and capabilities comes from observing children while they are actively engaged and from analyzing the products of their work. Whatever conclusions we may make about children's thinking must be based on **observations** or **products.**

The table below shows the different contexts for assessment and the sources of evidence used for each context. Specific assessment tasks in *Everyday Mathematics* are included. Use this table as a guide in designing your balanced assessment plan.

Sources of Evidence and Assessment Contexts

		Assessment Contexts		
		Ongoing Assessment	**Periodic Assessment**	**External Assessment**
Sources of Evidence	**Observation**	◆ Informing Instruction notes ◆ Recognizing Student Achievement notes for • Mental Math and Reflexes ◆ "Kid watching"	◆ Progress Check Oral/Slate Assessments	◆ Classroom observations by resource teachers or other outside experts
	Product	◆ Recognizing Student Achievement notes for • Journal pages • Exit Slips • Games record sheets • Math Boxes ◆ Writing/Reasoning prompts ◆ Portfolio opportunities	◆ Beginning-of-Year, Mid-Year, and End-of-Year assessments ◆ Progress Check Written Assessments ◆ Student Self Assessments ◆ Open Response problems	◆ Standardized tests mandated by the school district or the state

Each context for assessment (ongoing, periodic, or external) can yield evidence through observations or products.

◆ Observing children as they are doing their daily work can provide a great deal of information about their understandings, skills, and dispositions; this kind of ongoing observational assessment may be considered "kid watching."

◆ A written assessment that is included as part of a curriculum is an example of a periodic product assessment.

◆ A classroom visit by an outside expert who will observe particular children is an example of an external assessment using observational evidence.

What Content Is Assessed?

> *Assessment does not exist in isolation, but must be closely aligned with the goals of curriculum and instruction.*
>
> (Pellegrino, Chudowsky, and Glaser 2001, 36)

In recent years, national organizations and most states have issued detailed sets of learning goals and standards, which provide useful guidance about what content is important to learn and, therefore, important to assess. Aligning assessment, curriculum, and instruction with standards and goals increases coherence in the system and produces better outcomes. To help teachers understand the structure of *Everyday Mathematics* and therefore better understand what to assess, the authors developed Program Goals, which are organized by content strand and carefully articulated across the grades. Below are the six content strands and their related Program Goals.

Everyday Mathematics Program Goals

Number and Numeration
- Understand the meanings, uses, and representations of numbers
- Understand equivalent names for numbers
- Understand common numerical relations

Operations and Computation
- Compute accurately
- Make reasonable estimates
- Understand meanings of operations

Data and Chance
- Select and create appropriate graphical representations of collected or given data
- Analyze and interpret data
- Understand and apply basic concepts of probability

Measurement and Reference Frames
- Understand the systems and processes of measurement; use appropriate techniques, tools, units, and formulas in making measurements
- Use and understand reference frames

Geometry
- Investigate characteristics and properties of two- and three-dimensional geometric shapes
- Apply transformations and symmetry in geometric situations

Patterns, Functions, and Algebra
- Understand patterns and functions
- Use algebraic notation to represent and analyze situations and structures

Program Goals are threads that weave the curriculum together across grades. "Compute accurately," for example, is a Program Goal. Children in *Everyday Mathematics* are expected to compute accurately. The expectations for a child achieving this goal in Grade 2 are obviously different from what is expected from a child in Grade 6. For this reason, the Program Goals are further refined through Grade-Level Goals.

Grade-Level Goals are guideposts along trajectories of learning that span multiple years. They are the big ideas at each grade level; they do not capture all of the content covered. The Grade-Level Goals describe how *Everyday Mathematics* builds mastery over time—first through informal exposure, later through more formal instruction, and finally through application. Because the Grade-Level Goals are cumulative, it is essential for students to experience the complete curriculum at each grade level. The example below shows the development of Grade-Level Goals for models for the operations.

Grade K	Identify join and take-away situations.
Grade 1	Identify change-to-more, change-to-less, comparison, and parts-and-total situations.
Grade 2	Identify and describe change, comparison, and parts-and-total situations; use repeated addition, arrays, and skip counting to model multiplication; use equal sharing and equal grouping to model division.
Grade 3	Recognize and describe change, comparison, and parts-and-total situations; use repeated addition, arrays, and skip counting to model multiplication; use equal sharing and equal grouping to model division.
Grade 4	Use repeated addition, skip counting, arrays, area, and scaling to model multiplication and division.
Grade 5	Use repeated addition, arrays, area, and scaling to model multiplication and division; use ratios expressed as words, fractions, percents, and with colons; solve problems involving ratios of parts of a set to the whole set.
Grade 6	Use ratios and scaling to model size changes and to solve size-change problems; represent ratios as fractions, percents, and decimals, and using a colon; model and solve problems involving part-to-whole and part-to-part ratios; model rate and ratio number stories with proportions; use and explain cross multiplication and other strategies to solve proportions.

All assessment opportunities in *Everyday Mathematics* are linked to specific Grade-Level Goals. The curriculum is designed so that the vast majority of students will reach the Grade-Level Goals for a given grade upon completion of that grade and as a result will be well prepared to succeed in higher levels of mathematics. The complete list of Program Goals and Grade-Level Goals begins on page 37 of this handbook.

Creating a Balanced Assessment Plan

In *Everyday Mathematics,* assessment is primarily designed to help you

◆ learn about children's current knowledge and abilities so you can plan future instruction more effectively—formative assessment; and
◆ measure children's progress toward and achievement of Grade-Level Goals—summative assessment.

Although there is no one right assessment plan for all classrooms, all assessment plans should provide a balance of assessment sources from different contexts. See the chart on page 4 of this handbook for specific assessment tasks in *Everyday Mathematics* that support the different sources and contexts.

Planning Tips

Do not try to use all the assessment resources at once. Instead, devise a manageable, balanced plan. Choose those tools and techniques that best match your teaching style and your children's needs.

Consider the following guidelines:

◆ Start small.
◆ Incorporate assessment into your daily class routine.
◆ Set up an easy and efficient record-keeping system.
◆ Personalize and adapt the plan as the year progresses.

Your assessment plan should be designed to answer these questions:

◆ How is the class doing?
◆ How are individual children doing?
◆ How do I need to adjust instruction to meet children's needs?
◆ How can I communicate to children, parents, and others about the progress being made?

The following sections of this handbook provide further details about the tools and techniques you can use to develop a balanced assessment plan. Using these tools, you can support children's learning, improve your instruction, measure children's growth and achievement, and make the most of your experience with *Everyday Mathematics.*

Ongoing Assessment

An integral part of a balanced assessment plan involves gathering information from children's everyday work. Opportunities for collecting ongoing assessment in the form of observations and products are highlighted in *Everyday Mathematics* through Informing Instruction and Recognizing Student Achievement notes.

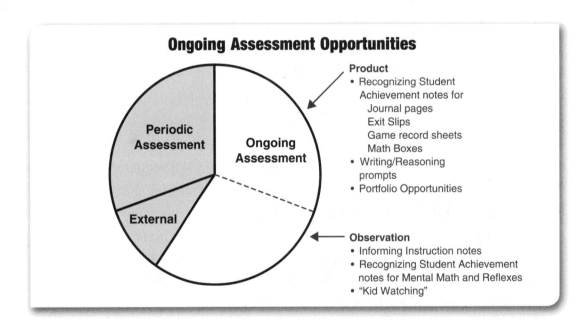

Ongoing Assessment Opportunities

- Periodic Assessment
- Ongoing Assessment
- External

Product
- Recognizing Student Achievement notes for
    Journal pages
    Exit Slips
    Game record sheets
    Math Boxes
- Writing/Reasoning prompts
- Portfolio Opportunities

Observation
- Informing Instruction notes
- Recognizing Student Achievement notes for Mental Math and Reflexes
- "Kid Watching"

Ongoing Assessment— Informing Instruction

Informing Instruction notes are designed to help you anticipate and recognize common errors and misconceptions in children's thinking and alert you to multiple solution strategies or unique insights that children may offer. These notes suggest how to use observations of children's work to effectively adapt instruction.

 Sample 1 Informing Instruction

 Ongoing Assessment: Informing Instruction

Watch for children who think parallel line segments only go in one direction. Have children draw parallel line segments on paper and then rotate the paper so they can see that the line segments remain parallel regardless of the direction.

 Sample 2 Informing Instruction

Ongoing Assessment: Informing Instruction

Watch for children who have difficulty adding more than two numbers. Remind them to find complements of multiples of 10. Provide a number grid for children to use as a tool.

Ongoing Assessment— Recognizing Student Achievement

Each lesson in *Everyday Mathematics* contains a Recognizing Student Achievement note. These notes highlight specific tasks that teachers can use for assessment to monitor children's progress toward Grade-Level Goals.

These tasks include:

◆ Journal pages (written problems—sometimes including explanations)
◆ Mental Math and Reflexes (oral or slate)
◆ Exit Slips (explanations of strategies and understanding)
◆ *Everyday Mathematics* games (record sheets or follow-up sheets)
◆ Math Boxes (written practice problems)

Each Recognizing Student Achievement note identifies the task to gather information from, the concept or skill to be assessed, and the expectations for a child who is *making adequate progress* toward meeting the specific Grade-Level Goal.

Sample 1 Recognizing Student Achievement
Math Journal 1

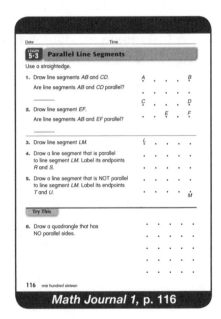

Ongoing Assessment:
Recognizing Student Achievement

Journal page 116
Problems
1 and 2

Use **journal page 116, Problems 1 and 2** to assess children's ability to identify parallel lines. Children are making adequate progress if they are able to use a straightedge to connect the points to make line segments and recognize that they are parallel. Some children may be able to successfully complete Problem 5 and draw a line segment that is not parallel to the others.

[Geometry Goal 1]

Math Journal 1, p. 116

Sample 2 **Recognizing Student Achievement**
Mental Math and Reflexes

 Ongoing Assessment: Mental Math and Reflexes
Recognizing Student Achievement

Use **Mental Math and Reflexes** to assess children's progress toward solving problems involving addition of multidigit multiples of ten. Children are making adequate progress if they are able to successfully complete Level 1. Some children may be able to solve problems that have a 4-digit number as a sum.

[Operations and Computation Goal 2]

Mental Math ★ and Reflexes

Pose pairs of problems, such as the following:

●○○   30 + 40 = ? 70
      300 + 400 = ? 700
●●○   ? = 20 + 50   70
      ? = 200 + 500   700
●●●   90 + 30 = ? 120
      900 + 300 = ? 1,200

 Sample 3 **Recognizing Student Achievement**
Exit Slip

 Ongoing Assessment: Exit Slip
Recognizing Student Achievement

Use an **Exit Slip** (*Math Masters,* page 415) to have children record the facts in the boxes for which they have at least one check mark. Children are making adequate progress if they record most of the facts in the Fact Power Table. Some children may record all the facts.

[Operations and Computation Goal 1]

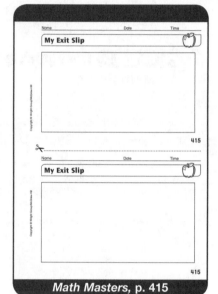

Math Masters, p. 415

Sample 4 Recognizing Student Achievement
Game Record Sheet

 Ongoing Assessment:
Recognizing Student Achievement

Journal page 163

Use the record sheet for *Hit the Target* on **journal page 163** to assess children's ability to find the difference between 2-digit numbers and any higher multiple of 10. Children are making adequate progress if they successfully complete Round 1 with or without the use of manipulatives. Some children may solve all problems without using manipulatives.

[Operations and Computation Goal 2]

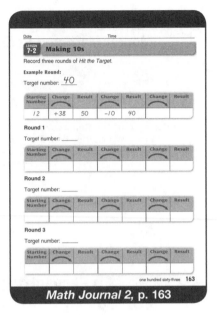

Math Journal 2, p. 163

 Sample 5 Recognizing Student Achievement
Math Boxes

 Ongoing Assessment:
Recognizing Student Achievement

Math Boxes Problem 3

Use **Math Boxes, Problem 3** to assess children's understanding of equal shares. Children are making adequate progress if they are able to complete the box accurately using counters or drawings.

[Operations and Computation Goal 4]

3. Get 36 counters. Share them equally among 4 children.

How many counters does each child get? _____ counters

How many are left over?

_____ counters

The Recognizing Student Achievement tasks were chosen with the expectation that the majority of children will be successful with them. Children who are *making adequate progress* as defined by a Recognizing Student Achievement task are on a trajectory to meet the corresponding Grade-Level Goal. Based on student progress toward Grade-Level Goals, you may choose to use Readiness activities or Enrichment activities to modify your instructional plan to meet an individual child's needs. See the chart on the next page for how to understand and use the results of the Recognizing Student Achievement tasks.

Using the Results of Recognizing Student Achievement Tasks

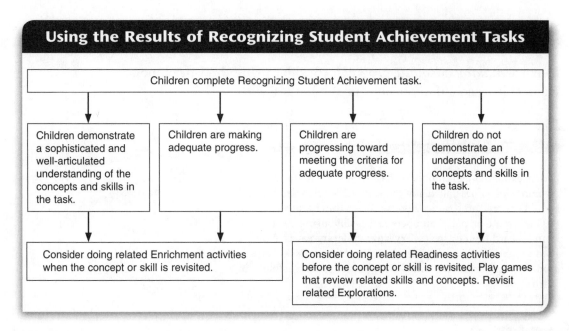

Children complete Recognizing Student Achievement task.

| Children demonstrate a sophisticated and well-articulated understanding of the concepts and skills in the task. | Children are making adequate progress. | Children are progressing toward meeting the criteria for adequate progress. | Children do not demonstrate an understanding of the concepts and skills in the task. |

Consider doing related Enrichment activities when the concept or skill is revisited.

Consider doing related Readiness activities before the concept or skill is revisited. Play games that review related skills and concepts. Revisit related Explorations.

Sample **Recognizing Student Achievement**

The following example illustrates how to implement further Enrichment or Readiness for a given Recognizing Student Achievement task.

 Ongoing Assessment:
Recognizing Student Achievement

Journal page 53
Problems
1 and 3 ★

Use **journal page 53, Problems 1 and 3** to assess children's understanding of place value. Children are making adequate progress if they can correctly answer the problems using base-10 blocks. Some children may be able to complete the problems that involve 0 as a placeholder.

[Number and Numeration Goal 2]

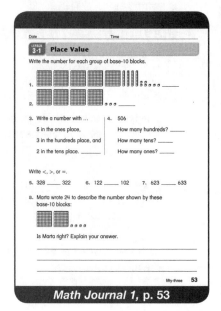

Math Journal 1, p. 53

 **Sample** **Enrichment**

If children are *making adequate progress,* consider using the Enrichment activities in this lesson, if applicable, or related lessons.

ENRICHMENT

▶ Creating 3-Digit Numbers

SMALL-GROUP ACTIVITY
🕐 5–15 Min

To further explore 3-digit numbers, have children create as many 3-digit numbers as possible using the same three nonzero digits. Each child selects three cards from the Everything Math Deck (1–9). They create as many numbers as possible using the three cards and record their answers. Try three different cards. Ask: *How many combinations are possible using three cards?* 6 Have children try four cards. How many combinations are possible using four cards? 24

 Sample **Readiness**

If children are *not making adequate progress,* consider using the Readiness activities before teaching related lessons.

READINESS

▶ Playing *Base-10 Exchange*

PARTNER ACTIVITY
🕐 5–15 Min

(*Math Masters,* p. 428)

To provide experience with place-value using a concrete model, have children play *Base-10 Exchange.*

▷ The bank starts with 20 longs and 40 cubes. Each player has a Place-Value Mat. They share a pair of dice.

▷ Players take turns. They roll the dice, announce the total number of dots, take that number of cubes from the bank, and place the cubes on the mat. Whenever possible, they exchange 10 cubes for 1 long. The player who is not rolling the dice checks the accuracy of the exchanges.

▷ The game ends when there are no more longs. The player with the most longs wins. If there is a tie, the player with the most cubes wins.

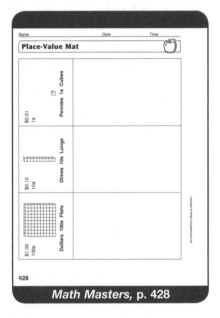

Math Masters, p. 428

Writing/Reasoning Prompts for Math Boxes

Every unit contains suggestions for prompts to use with Math Boxes problems. Use these prompts in a number of ways: (1) Collect children's responses to these prompts on Exit Slips. (2) Request that children keep a math notebook where they record their answers to Math Message problems, Exit Slip prompts, and Writing/Reasoning prompts for Math Boxes problems. (3) Have children record responses on Math Log or Exit Slip masters and then add them to their portfolio collections.

Sample 1 **Writing/Reasoning Prompt**

Writing/Reasoning Have children draw, write, or verbalize their answers to the following: *Explain why the number of nickels in $3.00 is double the number of dimes in $3.00.* Sample answer: A nickel is worth 5 cents and a dime is worth 10 cents. 5 is half of 10.

1. _____ pennies = $3.00

   _____ nickels = $3.00

   _____ dimes = $3.00

   _____ quarters = $3.00

Sample 2 **Writing/Reasoning Prompt**

Writing/Reasoning Have children draw, write, or verbalize their answers to the following: *Explain how you know that you made the largest number in Problem 1.* Sample answer: I picked the largest digit to be in the hundreds place, the second largest digit to be in the tens place, and the smallest digit to be in the ones place. Then I tested 531 against the other combinations and it was the largest number.

1. Use the digits 1, 3, and 5 to make:

   the smallest number possible.

   _____

   the largest number possible.

   _____

Portfolios

Portfolios are a versatile tool for student assessment. They help children reflect on their mathematical growth and help you understand and document that growth. Portfolios are part of a balanced assessment plan in that they:

◆ emphasize progress over time;

◆ involve children more directly in the assessment process as they participate in selecting work and explaining what the work demonstrates; and

◆ document strengths and weaknesses in a child's mathematical development.

is the symbol used to indicate opportunities to collect children's work for portfolios. Several portfolio opportunities are highlighted in each unit, but in addition to highlighted opportunities, you and your children can choose from the variety of work in daily lessons to add to children's portfolios.

Consider asking children to write about their selected works. Two optional masters, Good Work and My Work, are provided for this.

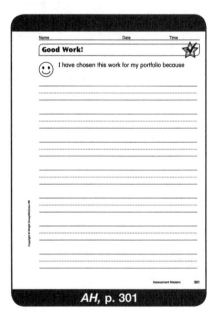

AH, p. 301

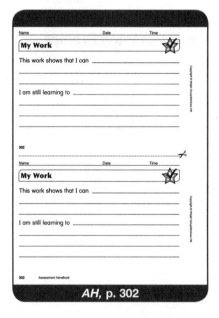

AH, p. 302

See pages 295–303 in this book for additional masters that you might ask children to complete periodically and incorporate into their portfolios. *For example:*

- ◆ Math Log A   ◆ About My Math Class A
- ◆ Math Log B   ◆ About My Math Class B
- ◆ Math Log C

You may also ask parents to complete a Parent Reflections page (*Assessment Handbook,* page 294) for inclusion in children's portfolios.

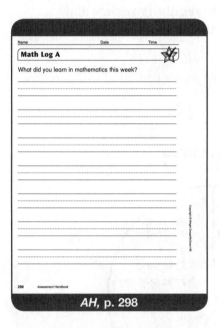

AH, p. 298

AH, p. 300

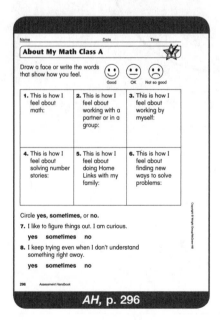

AH, p. 296

AH, p. 297

Periodic Assessment

Periodic assessments are another key component of a balanced assessment plan. Progress Check lessons and Beginning-of-Year, Mid-Year, and End-of-Year assessments require children to complete a variety of tasks, including short answer questions, open response problems, and reflection questions. These tasks provide you and your children with the opportunity to regularly review and reflect upon their progress—in areas that were recently introduced as well as in areas that involve long-term retention and mastery.

The figure below lists the various periodic assessment tasks provided in *Everyday Mathematics*.

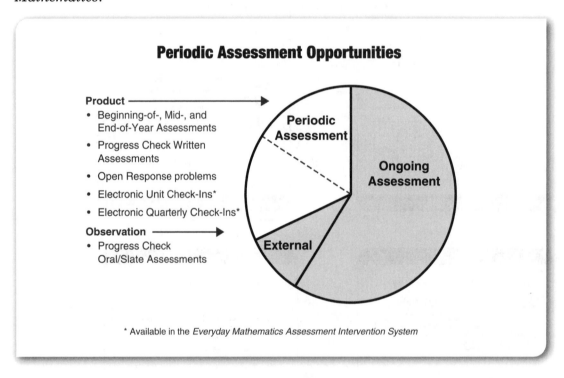

Periodic Assessment Opportunities

Product
- Beginning-of-, Mid-, and End-of-Year Assessments
- Progress Check Written Assessments
- Open Response problems
- Electronic Unit Check-Ins*
- Electronic Quarterly Check-Ins*

Observation
- Progress Check Oral/Slate Assessments

Periodic Assessment

Ongoing Assessment

External

* Available in the *Everyday Mathematics Assessment Intervention System*

Progress Check Written Assessments

Each Progress Check lesson includes a Written Assessment incorporating tasks that address content from lessons in the current and previous units. The Grade-Level Goals addressed in the Written Assessment are listed at the beginning of the lesson. These assessments provide information for evaluating student progress and planning for future instruction.

Written Assessments are one way children demonstrate what they know. Maximize opportunities for children to show the breadth of their knowledge on these assessments by adapting questions as appropriate. Beginning on page 51 in the unit-specific section of this handbook, there are suggested modifications for the Written Assessments that will allow you to tailor questions and get a more accurate picture of what children know.

Experts in assessment distinguish between summative and formative purposes of assessment. Summative assessment measures student growth and achievement so you can determine whether children have learned certain material. Formative assessment provides information about children's current knowledge and abilities so you can plan future instruction more effectively.

Accordingly, all *Everyday Mathematics* Progress Check written assessments include two parts:

◆ Part A is designed for summative purposes. The questions provide teachers with information on how children are progressing toward Grade-Level Goals. The questions can be used in the same way as Recognizing Student Achievement notes. Children *making adequate progress* toward Grade-Level Goals should do fairly well on this section.

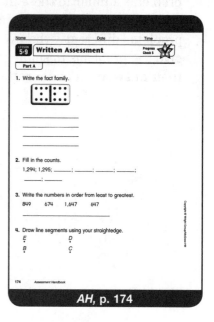

AH, p. 174

◆ Part B is designed for formative purposes. The questions can be used to establish baselines for documenting student growth over time. The questions also assist teachers in their long-term planning in the same way as Informing Instruction notes help teachers in planning lessons.

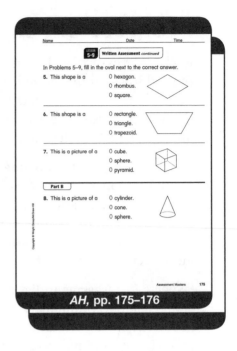

AH, pp. 175–176

Oral and Slate Assessment

Each Progress Check lesson features an Oral and Slate Assessment that includes problems similar to those in Mental Math and Reflexes, which appears in each lesson. You may choose to manage the collection of information from these problems differently than you do with the daily practice. For example, you may give the problems to small groups of children at a time or have children record their answers on paper rather than on slates.

Student Self Assessment

Each Progress Check lesson includes a Self Assessment master that children complete. These Self Assessments are part of a balanced assessment plan as they allow:

◆ children to reflect on their progress, strengths, and weaknesses;
◆ teachers to gain insights into how children perceive their progress; and
◆ teachers and children to plan how to address weaknesses.

The Self Assessment engages children in evaluating their competency with the concepts and skills addressed in the unit. For each skill or concept, children check a box to indicate one of the following:

◆ I can do this by myself. I can explain how to do this.
◆ I can do this by myself.
◆ I can do this with help.

If children feel as though they need help or do not understand, consider talking with them about how they may learn more about the concept or skill. Look to related Readiness activities in Part 3 of lessons and to games for ideas about further developing children's understanding.

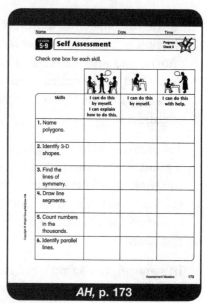

AH, p. 173

Open Response Tasks

Each Progress Check lesson includes an Open Response task linked to one or more Grade-Level Goals emphasized in the unit. These Open Response assessment tasks can provide additional balance in an assessment plan as they allow children to:

◆ become more aware of their problem-solving processes as they communicate their understanding, for example, through words, pictures, or diagrams;
◆ apply a variety of strategies to solve the longer tasks;
◆ further demonstrate their knowledge and understanding through application of skills and concepts in meaningful contexts; and
◆ be successful on a variety of levels.

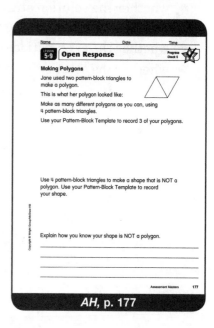

AH, p. 177

The Open Response tasks have been selected with the following points in mind:

◆ The problem context makes sense to children.
◆ The skill level of the problem is appropriate for children.
◆ The problem involves mathematics in which children have a foundation.
◆ The mathematics of the problem is important to the grade level. The problem addresses one or more Grade-Level Goals for the grade.
◆ The problem has connections to the real world that children have experience with.
◆ The problem may not be a multistep problem, but the solution strategy involves several steps.
◆ The problem may have more than one correct solution.

In the unit-specific section of this handbook that begins on page 51, each Open Response task has suggested implementation strategies, a sample task-specific rubric, and annotated children's samples demonstrating the expectations described in the rubric. The unit-specific section also includes suggestions for adapting the Open Response task to meet the needs of a diverse group of children.

The sample rubrics are on a 4-point scale. The top two scores (4 points and 3 points) are designated for student work that demonstrates success with the task. The bottom two scores (2 points and 1 point) are designated for student work that does not demonstrate success with the task; 0 points are reserved for situations where children have made no effort to understand or solve the problem.

In general, the sample rubrics focus on assessing the following items:

◆ whether the mathematics children use is correct;
◆ whether the solution strategy makes sense, is reasonable, addresses the problem, and may lead to a successful solution;
◆ whether the explanation of the strategy is clear and easy to follow; and
◆ whether the solution is correct (or correct except for minor errors).

Making Polygons Rubric

4	Records at least three polygons and at least one figure that is not a polygon. Uses four pattern-block triangles in all figures. Clearly explains at least one attribute that defines the figure as not being a polygon. Uses mathematical vocabulary such as *sides, cross, meet, space,* and *gaps.*
3	Records at least three polygons and at least one figure that is not a polygon. Uses four pattern-block triangles in most figures. The explanation provides evidence of some understanding of the attributes of polygons, but it might be difficult to relate to the figure that is not a polygon.
2	Records some figures as polygons, but all of them might not be polygons. Attempts to record a figure that is not a polygon. Some figures might use four pattern-block triangles. The explanation shows evidence of some understanding of the attributes of polygons, but it is incomplete or does not apply to the figure that is not a polygon.
1	Records some figures, but they might not be correct for each part of the problem. Some figures might use four pattern-block triangles. The explanation might not make sense in the context of the problem, or it might be missing.
0	Does not attempt to understand or solve the problem.

You may want to work with other teachers from your grade level to apply the *Everyday Mathematics* rubric to your children's work or to create rubrics for scoring these tasks. Consider the expectations of standardized tests in your area when creating or applying a rubric and modify this sample rubric as appropriate. For more child involvement, consider having children participate in developing a list of expectations for a Level-4 paper.

Beginning-of-Year, Mid-Year, and End-of-Year Assessments

To provide a snapshot of how children are progressing toward a broader range of Grade-Level Goals, the program includes three assessments at each grade level—Beginning-of-Year, Mid-Year, and End-of-Year. These assessments cover important concepts and skills presented throughout the year. The Beginning-of-Year, Mid-Year, and End-of-Year assessments provide additional information that you may wish to include in developing your balanced assessment plan.

In order to be successful with these assessments, some children, especially children in Grades 1 and 2, may benefit from having problems read aloud to them. Consider administering these assessments over two or more days. And, as with all *Everyday Mathematics* assessments, provide children with tools that may be helpful in completing the assessment. In some cases, problems suggest tools that can be used, but in other cases simply having access to manipulatives, such as counters or a number line, is enough to provide children access to the content.

External Assessment

Outside tests, which are one example of external assessment, are generally tests given at the school, district, or state level, or are nationally standardized tests. Most teachers are familiar with the standardized tests that have multiple-choice responses. The frustrating aspect of this type of test is that it analyzes a narrow range of mathematical thinking and does not assess the depth and breadth of the mathematical knowledge that should be attained in a well-implemented *Everyday Mathematics* classroom.

Everyday Mathematics can help your children function more effectively in testing environments. For example, some Math Boxes problems have been tailored to help prepare children for the formats of an outside test. Even without such preparation, *Everyday Mathematics* students generally do just as well on the computation sections of standardized tests. However, they do much better on concepts and problem-solving sections than children in traditional programs.

More recently, some district and state tests have included performance assessments or open-ended components. *Everyday Mathematics* presents varied mathematics tasks that prepare children for these testing situations: problems requiring children to explain their thinking, writing prompts designed to help children explore content more deeply, and richer Open Response tasks that may require an entire class period for children to solve. If you have a choice in your district, encourage the use of these performance-based or open-ended assessments. They better depict the depth of your children's understandings, as well as their abilities to communicate mathematically, solve problems, and reason.

Performance-based assessments developed at the school or district level probably provide the best opportunities to gather information about student achievement in local classrooms. Teams of teachers and administrators can develop assessments and rubrics that enhance the learning process rather than focus on narrow thinking used only in a small portion of mathematical activities. At some grade levels, these assessments can be used exclusively. When standardized testing is mandatory at a certain grade level, performance-based assessments can provide a better picture of the mathematical education occurring in the classroom than other types of standardized tests.

Record Keeping

If you teach *Everyday Mathematics* as intended and use the techniques described in this book, you will soon have a vast amount of information about children's mathematical skills and understanding. This section of the handbook offers several tools to help you organize and record this information.

Class Checklists and Individual Profiles of Progress

Each lesson in *Everyday Mathematics* identifies a suggested ongoing assessment opportunity in the form of a Recognizing Student Achievement note. These notes highlight specific tasks from which teachers can collect student performance data to monitor and document children's progress toward meeting specific Grade-Level Goals. Each unit in *Everyday Mathematics* contains a Progress Check lesson with suggested periodic assessment tasks. A wealth of assessment information can be collected from these and other sources.

To help you keep track of children's progress in areas that are important to your school and district, checklists for individuals and for the class are provided beginning on page 236 of this handbook. There are Class Checklists for each unit and for each quarter. There are Individual Profiles of Progress for each unit. These checklists provide an organizational system for recording the information you collect to assess student progress on Grade-Level Goals.

The unit checklists include places to record information gathered from the Recognizing Student Achievement notes and from the Progress Check lesson in the unit. The checklists identify the related Grade-Level Goal for each Recognizing Student Achievement task. There is an additional column in which you can add your comments or other notes. To simplify data entry, these checklists are organized according to lesson number.

The quarterly checklists include places to record information gathered throughout the quarter from the Recognizing Student Achievement tasks. To simplify the process of aggregating data in meaningful ways, these checklists are organized according to mathematical strand.

You may prefer using the Class Checklists (on the right) to gather and organize information, transferring selected information to the Individual Profiles of Progress sheet for each child's portfolio or for use during parent conferences.

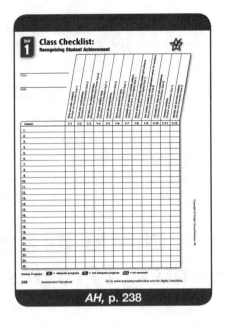

AH, p. 238

Checklist Flow Chart

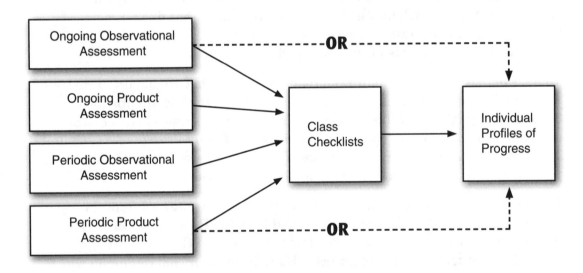

The Individual Profiles of Progress, Class Checklists, and Quarterly Checklists can be found in the Assessment Masters beginning on page 236 of this handbook. Blank checklists have been provided as well. Assessment checklists are also available online at www.everydaymathonline.com.

Options for Recording Data on Checklists

There are several different record-keeping schemes for checklists. Two such schemes are described below.

Option 1

Because Recognizing Student Achievement suggestions include descriptions of the expectations for *making adequate progress,* consider recording this information on a checklist using the following:

A	Child is making adequate progress toward Grade-Level Goal.
N	Child is not making adequate progress toward Grade-Level Goal.

or

✔	Child is making adequate progress toward Grade-Level Goal.
–	Child is not making adequate progress toward Grade-Level Goal.

Option 2

As the teacher, you can decide how you define what is *making adequate progress* and what is not. For example, if you use a 4-point rubric like the sample below, you may decide to define 3 or 4 points as *making adequate progress* and 1 or 2 points as *not making adequate progress.*

4 points	Child is making adequate progress. Child solves the problem correctly and demonstrates a sophisticated and well-articulated understanding of the concept or skill being assessed.
3 points	Child is making adequate progress. Child solves the problem correctly with only minor errors and demonstrates a developmentally appropriate understanding of the concept or skill being assessed.
2 points	Child is not making adequate progress. Child appears to understand some components of the problem and attempts to solve the problem. Child demonstrates an understanding of the concept or skill being assessed that is marginally short of what is expected.
1 point	Child is not making adequate progress. Child appears to not understand the problem but makes some attempt to solve it. Child demonstrates an understanding of the concept or skill being assessed that is significantly short of what is expected.
0 points	Child does not attempt to solve the problem.

Assessment Management Spreadsheets

Introduction

The digital *Everyday Mathematics Assessment Management Spreadsheets* are designed to help you track and record information about children's progress towards the *Everyday Mathematics* Grade-Level Goals and the Common Core State Standards. This application contains digital versions of all of the Class Checklists and Individual Profiles of Progress located at the back of this book and can be found at www.everydaymathonline.com.

Everyday Mathematics: Common Core State Standards Edition was designed so the vast majority of children will be successful in mastering the Common Core State Standards and the *Everyday Mathematics* Grade-Level Goals for a given grade upon completion of that grade. Each assessment task provides a snapshot of a child's progress toward the corresponding Grade-Level Goal(s). Taken together, these snapshots form a moving picture that can help you assess whether a child is on a trajectory, or path, to meet the Grade-Level Goal.

Record Keeping

You can use the digital *Everyday Mathematics Assessment Management Spreadsheets* to enter children's performance information for the following assessment types:

◆ Ongoing Assessment: Recognizing Student Achievement
◆ Progress Check: Oral and Slate
◆ Progress Check: Written Assessment Parts A and B
◆ Progress Check: Open Response
◆ Beginning-of-Year Assessment
◆ Mid-Year Assessment
◆ End-of-Year Assessment

You can also easily complement the assessments provided in *Everyday Mathematics* by adding children's performance data from tasks you design or from the many other tasks in the *Everyday Mathematics* curriculum.

Grading Assistance

While grading is not the primary goal of the *Everyday Mathematics Assessment Management Spreadsheets,* the tool can assist you in assigning grades and creating report cards. You can use it to record children's progress on many types of assessment tasks, including those that you create, so your evidence for assessment is based on multiple sources. These records of children's performance, combined with the careful observations you make about your children's work, will help you assign fair and accurate grades.

Using the Digital *Assessment Management Spreadsheets*

The digital *Assessment Management Spreadsheets* include many features for supporting your balanced assessment plan. *For example:*

◆ All the suggested *Everyday Mathematics* assessment tasks are built into the system. Selecting a unit number will bring you to a screen that mirrors the Class Checklist masters, which list all the assessment tasks in a given unit.

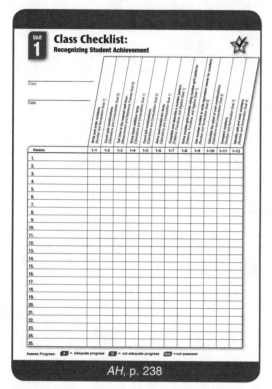
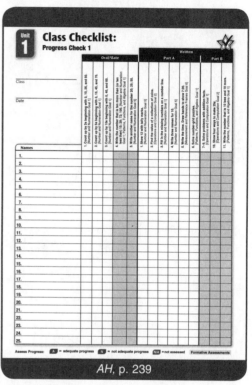

AH, p. 238   *AH,* p. 239

Digital versions of these checklists for all units are available through the Assessment Management Spreadsheets, *found at www.everydaymathonline.com.*

◆ A digital version of the Individual Profile of Progress can be automatically generated from the digital class checklists. You can add text comments for individual children on the digital Individual Profile of Progress.

◆ Teacher-created tasks can be added to the digital spreadsheets.

◆ In addition to classifying children's performance as "making adequate progress" or "not making adequate progress," there is a 0- to 4-point (detailed) scoring option. The detailed scoring option can be used for all assessments or just for open-response items. You can determine the level of specificity that best suits your assessment needs.

For assistance with the *Assessment Management Spreadsheets* and specific feature instructions, click the Help link at the top of any screen within the tool.

Frequently Asked Questions

1. **Do the Grade-Level Goals summarize all the concepts and skills that are covered each year?**

   No; Although the Grade-Level Goals reflect the core of the curriculum at each grade level, they are not comprehensive. They do not capture all the content that is addressed each year. Nor are they a list of activities that are completed each year. Some grade-level content supports future Grade-Level Goals that are not articulated at the given grade level.

2. **With all these Grade-Level Goals, how will I know when I'm simply exposing children to a concept or skill?**

   The *Everyday Mathematics* curriculum aims for student proficiency with concepts and skills through repeated exposures over several years. The *Teacher's Lesson Guide* alerts teachers to content that is being introduced for the first time through Links to the Future notes. These notes provide specific references to future Grade-Level Goals and help teachers understand introductory activities at their grade levels in the context of the entire K–6 curriculum.

   All the content in *Everyday Mathematics* is important, whether it's being experienced for the first or the fifth time. The *Everyday Mathematics* curriculum is similar to an intricately woven rug, with many threads that appear and reappear to form complex patterns. Different children will progress at different rates, so multiple exposures to important content are critical for accommodating individual differences. The program was created so it is consistent with how children learn mathematics. It builds understanding over a period of time, first through informal exposure and later through more formal and directed instruction. For children to succeed, they need the opportunity to experience all that the curriculum has to offer in every grade.

3. **There are a lot of lessons in my grade-level materials. Do I have to finish all of them? For example, I teach second grade. Automaticity with multiplication facts is not a Grade-Level Goal until third grade. Can't I just skip all of the second-grade lessons that cover multiplication facts?**

Everyday Mathematics was created to be consistent with how children actually learn mathematics, building understanding over time, first through informal exposure and later through more formal instruction. Because the Grade-Level Goals are cumulative, it is essential for children to experience the complete curriculum at each grade level. Children in *Second Grade Everyday Mathematics,* for example, participate in many hands-on activities designed to develop an understanding of multiplication. This makes it possible for children to achieve multiplication goals in third grade.

4. **Do I need to keep track of progress on Program Goals?**

Program Goals are the threads that weave the content together across grade levels and form the skeleton of the curriculum. The Program Goals are further refined through the Grade-Level Goals. *Everyday Mathematics* provides a variety of tools you can use to assess student progress on the Grade-Level Goals throughout the year. Because every Grade-Level Goal is related to a Program Goal, you are gathering information at this less-specific level as well. This allows great flexibility in reporting to parents. Depending on how your district requires you to aggregate data, you can look broadly at strands, more closely at Program Goals, or specifically at Grade-Level Goals using the suggested assessments in *Everyday Mathematics.*

5. **What do the authors mean by "adequate progress"?**

Children who are making adequate progress as defined by a Recognizing Student Achievement note are on a trajectory to meet the Grade-Level Goal. Such children have successfully accomplished what is expected up to that point in the curriculum. If children continue to progress as expected, then they will demonstrate proficiency with the Grade-Level Goal upon completion of the year.

The performance expectations described in the Recognizing Student Achievement notes for any given Grade-Level Goal progress developmentally throughout the year. The level of performance that is expected in October is not the same as what is expected in April. The term *adequate progress* describes the level of competency that the majority of children can be expected to have at a particular time. The authors of *Everyday Mathematics* chose the Recognizing Student Achievement tasks with the expectation that the majority of children would be successful with them, which is in line with the expectation that the vast majority of children will successfully reach the Grade-Level Goals for their grade level.

6. **Do children have to complete all the Recognizing Student Achievement tasks before I can know whether they are making adequate progress?**

Each lesson in *Everyday Mathematics* contains a Recognizing Student Achievement note. These notes highlight specific tasks from which teachers can collect student performance data to monitor and document children's progress toward meeting specific Grade-Level Goals. Each Recognizing Student Achievement note addresses part of a Grade-Level Goal. The suggested assessment tasks build a complete picture over time for each Grade-Level Goal. If children perform well on one or two Recognizing Student Achievement tasks for a goal, that may not provide enough information about the goal in its entirety. Teachers are the experts in their classrooms. If you choose to not do some of the Recognizing Student Achievement tasks, consider collecting similar information from tasks you designate to assemble a complete picture for each Grade-Level Goal.

7. **Can I use only Math Boxes to collect assessment information? They seem to have all the skills in them.**

Everyday Mathematics includes a variety of assessment tasks to ensure that all children have sufficient opportunities to demonstrate what they know. Some children best demonstrate their knowledge through pencil-and-paper tasks, some through performance tasks, and some through explanations and demonstrations. The assessment tasks in the program have been chosen to accommodate a range of learners. Using only one tool might limit what you are able to learn about your children.

8. **I understand that *Everyday Mathematics* provides a Recognizing Student Achievement task for every lesson. May I choose my own instead of or in addition to the ones designated by the curriculum? If I don't think the results of a particular Recognizing Student Achievement task accurately reflect what a child knows, what should I do?**

The Recognizing Student Achievement tasks and Progress Check questions occur at carefully chosen points, based on the opportunities for distributed practice that occur throughout the program. Assessment tasks were also designed to vary the ways in which children are assessed for each Grade-Level Goal.

The *Everyday Mathematics* authors respect teachers as professionals and expect that teachers will use their professional judgment when assessing children. If a particular Recognizing Student Achievement task does not adequately assess student achievement, the teacher may choose to disregard it. The *Everyday Mathematics* authors also anticipate that children's performances on tasks that are not identified in Recognizing Student Achievement notes will often provide useful information regarding their progress toward a particular Grade-Level Goal. Teachers should feel free to link such tasks to appropriate Grade-Level Goals and include them in their assessment stories.

9. **I understand the different record-keeping options that were presented in this handbook. My district, however, evaluates children by assigning traditional letter grades. How should I evaluate student performance?**

Because local assessment systems are based on local norms and values, it would be impossible to design a system that would apply universally. But the authors of *Everyday Mathematics* recognize that many teachers are required by their districts to give traditional grades. And although it is impossible to design a single grading system that will work for everyone, there are some broad principles to follow:

◆ Grades should be fair and based on evidence that can be documented.
◆ Evidence for grading should come from multiple sources.
◆ Grades should be based on content that is important. They should not be based only on the content that is most easily assessed.
◆ The grading system should be aligned with both state and local standards and with the curriculum.

10. **Suppose a child makes adequate progress on the majority of Recognizing Student Achievement tasks and Progress Check questions for a given Grade-Level Goal throughout the year. At the end of the year how likely is it that the child will have achieved the Grade-Level Goal?**

The Recognizing Student Achievement and Progress Check tasks supply a great deal of data on which teachers can base inferences about children's achievement of Grade-Level Goals. In the case of a consistent pattern of adequate progress on assessment tasks for a given Grade-Level Goal, one can reasonably conclude that the child has in fact achieved the given goal. As with any assessment, however, inferences based on positive performance are more straightforward than those based on negative performance. That is, if a child performs well, the most straightforward conclusion is that the child has probably mastered the material; whereas if a child performs poorly, there are many possible explanations, only one of which is a lack of mastery.

Teachers should also recognize that inferences about what children know should always be considered provisional because the inferences are fallible, based as they are on incomplete information, and because children are constantly growing and changing.

According to *Knowing What Students Know*:

> . . . by its very nature, assessment is imprecise to some degree. Assessment results are estimates, based on samples of knowledge and performance drawn from the much larger universe of everything a person knows and can do. . . . Assessment is a process of reasoning from evidence. Because one cannot directly perceive students' mental processes, one must rely on less direct methods to make judgments about what they know.
>
> (Pellegrino, Chudowsky, and Glaser 2001, 36)
>
> An assessment is a tool designed to observe students' behavior and produce data that can be used to draw reasonable inferences about what students know.
>
> (Pellegrino, Chudowsky, and Glaser 2001, 42)

11. What about a child who normally performs well in class but does poorly on the electronic Check-Ins given after Quarters 2 and 4?

The electronic Check-Ins given after Quarters 2 and 4 are just one piece of the *Everyday Mathematics* assessment story; they are not meant to stand alone and do not provide a complete picture of a child's progress towards any one goal. Because they can be administered and scored electronically, they provide teachers with some relatively easy data collection. However, because the Check-Ins were written in multiple-choice format, they are limited in the information they can provide about what a child knows.

The pencil-and-paper Mid-Year and End-of-Year Assessments are the "best" assessments we offer in *Everyday Mathematics*. They are more comprehensive in their coverage of what children should be responsible for knowing at the time they are given. Children are able to show what they know in a variety of ways, and teachers can gather more information about a child by reviewing the work produced during one of these assessments.

We recommend that teachers administer all electronic and paper-and-pencil assessments. However, teachers worried about over-testing may choose to skip the review portion of the Quarter 2 Check-In, as the questions related to those goals are assessed in a more comprehensive manner on the Mid-Year Assessment.

Recommended Reading

Black, Paul, and Dylan Wiliam. "Assessment and Classroom Learning." *Assessment in Education* (March, 1998): 7–74.

_____. "Inside the Black Box: Raising Standards Through Classroom Assessment." *Phi Delta Kappan* 80, no. 2 (October, 1998): 139–149.

Bryant, Brian R., and Teddy Maddox. "Using Alternative Assessment Techniques to Plan and Evaluate Mathematics." *LD Forum 21,* no. 2 (winter, 1996): 24–33.

Eisner, Elliot W. "The Uses and Limits of Performance Assessment." *Phi Delta Kappan* 80, no. 9 (May, 1999): 658–661.

Kulm, Gerald. *Mathematics Assessment: What Works in the Classroom.* San Francisco: Jossey-Bass Publishers, 1994.

National Council of Teachers of Mathematics (NCTM). *Curriculum and Evaluation Standards for School Mathematics.* Reston, Va.: NCTM, 1989.

_____. *Assessment Standards for School Mathematics.* Reston, Va.: NCTM, 1995.

_____. *Principles and Standards for School Mathematics.* Reston, Va.: NCTM, 2000.

National Research Council. Committee on the Foundations of Assessment. Pellegrino, James W., Naomi Chudowsky, and Robert Glaser, eds. *Knowing What Students Know: The Science and Design of Educational Assessment.* Washington, D.C.: National Academy Press, 2001.

National Research Council, Mathematical Sciences Education Board. *Measuring What Counts: A Conceptual Guide for Mathematics Assessment.* Washington, D.C.: National Academy Press, 1993.

Pearson, Bethyl, and Cathy Berghoff. "London Bridge Is Not Falling Down: It's Supporting Alternative Assessment." *TESOL Journal* 5, no. 4 (summer, 1996): 28–31.

Shepard, Lorrie A. "Using Assessment to Improve Learning." *Educational Leadership* 52, no. 5 (February, 1995): 38–43.

Stenmark, Jean Kerr, ed. *Mathematics Assessment: Myths, Models, Good Questions, and Practical Suggestions.* Reston, Va.: National Council of Teachers of Mathematics, 1991.

Stiggens, Richard J. *Student-Centered Classroom Assessment.* Englewood Cliffs, N.J.: Prentice-Hall, 1997.

Webb, N. L., and A. F. Coxford, eds. *Assessment in the Mathematics Classroom: 1993 Yearbook.* Reston, Va.: National Council of Teachers of Mathematics, 1993.

http://everydaymath.uchicago.edu/

Everyday Mathematics GOALS

The following tables list the Grade-Level Goals organized by Content Strand and Program Goal.

Everyday Mathematics®

Content Strand: NUMBER AND NUMERATION

Program Goal: Understand the Meanings, Uses, and Representations of Numbers

Content	Kindergarten	First Grade	Second Grade	Third Grade	Fourth Grade	Fifth Grade	Sixth Grade
Rote counting	**Goal 1.** Count on by 1s to 100; count on by 2s, 5s, and 10s and count back by 1s with number grids, number lines, and calculators.	**Goal 1.** Count on by 1s, 2s, 5s, and 10s past 100 and count back by 1s from any number less than 100 with and without number grids, number lines, and calculators.	**Goal 1.** Count on by 1s, 2s, 5s, 10s, 25s, and 100s past 1,000 and back by 1s, 10s, and 100s from any number less than 1,000 with and without number grids, number lines, and calculators.				
Rational counting	**Goal 2.** Count 20 or more objects; estimate the number of objects in a collection.	**Goal 2.** Count collections of objects accurately and reliably; estimate the number of objects in a collection.					
Place value and notation	**Goal 3.** Model numbers with manipulatives; use manipulatives to exchange 1s for 10s and 10s for 100s; recognize that digits can be used and combined to read and write numbers; read numbers up to 30.	**Goal 3.** Read, write, and model with manipulatives whole numbers up to 1,000; identify places in such numbers and the values of the digits in those places.	**Goal 2.** Read, write, and model with manipulatives whole numbers up to 10,000; identify places in such numbers and the values of the digits in those places; read and write money amounts in dollars-and-cents notation.	**Goal 1.** Read and write whole numbers up to 1,000,000; read, write, and model with manipulatives decimals through hundredths; identify places in such numbers and the values of the digits in those places; translate between whole numbers and decimals represented in words, in base-10 notation, and with manipulatives.	**Goal 1.** Read and write whole numbers up to 1,000,000,000 and decimals through thousandths; identify places in such numbers and the values of the digits in those places; translate between whole numbers and decimals represented in words and in base-10 notation.	**Goal 1.** Read and write whole numbers and decimals; identify places in such numbers and the values of the digits in those places; use expanded notation to represent whole numbers and decimals.	**Goal 1.** Read and write whole numbers and decimals; identify places in such numbers and the values of the digits in those places; use expanded notation, number-and-word notation, exponential notation, and scientific notation to represent whole numbers and decimals.

Everyday Mathematics

Content Strand: NUMBER AND NUMERATION cont.

Program Goal: Understand the Meanings, Uses, and Representations of Numbers cont.

Content	Kindergarten	First Grade	Second Grade	Third Grade	Fourth Grade	Fifth Grade	Sixth Grade
Meanings and uses of fractions	**Goal 4.** Use manipulatives to model half of a region or a collection; describe the model.	**Goal 4.** Use manipulatives and drawings to model halves, thirds, and fourths as equal parts of a region or a collection; describe the model.	**Goal 3.** Use manipulatives and drawings to model fractions as equal parts of a region or a collection; describe the models and name the fractions.	**Goal 2.** Read, write, and model fractions; solve problems involving fractional parts of a region or a collection; describe strategies used.	**Goal 2.** Read, write, and model fractions; solve problems involving fractional parts of a region or a collection; describe and explain strategies used; given a fractional part of a region or a collection, identify the unit whole.	**Goal 2.** Solve problems involving percents and discounts; describe and explain strategies used; identify the unit whole in situations involving fractions.	**Goal 2.** Solve problems involving percents and discounts; explain strategies used; identify the unit whole in situations involving fractions, decimals, and percents.
Number theory		**Goal 5.** Use manipulatives to identify and model odd and even numbers.	**Goal 4.** Recognize numbers as odd or even.	**Goal 3.** Find multiples of 2, 5, and 10.	**Goal 3.** Find multiples of whole numbers less than 10; identify prime and composite numbers; find whole-number factors of numbers.	**Goal 3.** Identify prime and composite numbers; factor numbers; find prime factorizations.	**Goal 3.** Use GCFs, LCMs, and divisibility rules to manipulate fractions.

Program Goal: Understand Equivalent Names for Numbers

Content	Kindergarten	First Grade	Second Grade	Third Grade	Fourth Grade	Fifth Grade	Sixth Grade
Equivalent names for whole numbers	**Goal 5.** Use manipulatives, drawings, and numerical expressions involving addition and subtraction of 1-digit numbers to give equivalent names for whole numbers up to 20.	**Goal 6.** Use manipulatives, drawings, tally marks, and numerical expressions involving addition and subtraction of 1- or 2-digit numbers to give equivalent names for whole numbers up to 100.	**Goal 5.** Use tally marks, arrays, and numerical expressions involving addition and subtraction to give equivalent names for whole numbers.	**Goal 4.** Use numerical expressions involving one or more of the basic four arithmetic operations to give equivalent names for whole numbers.	**Goal 4.** Use numerical expressions involving one or more of the basic four arithmetic operations and grouping symbols to give equivalent names for whole numbers.	**Goal 4.** Use numerical expressions involving one or more of the basic four arithmetic operations, grouping symbols, and exponents to give equivalent names for whole numbers; convert between base-10, exponential, and repeated-factor notations.	**Goal 4.** Apply the order of operations to numerical expressions to give equivalent names for rational numbers.

Everyday Mathematics

Content Strand: NUMBER AND NUMERATION *cont.*

Program Goal: Understand Equivalent Names for Numbers *cont.*

Content	Kindergarten	First Grade	Second Grade	Third Grade	Fourth Grade	Fifth Grade	Sixth Grade
Equivalent names for fractions, decimals, and percents			**Goal 6.** Use manipulatives and drawings to model equivalent names for $\frac{1}{2}$.	**Goal 5.** Use manipulatives and drawings to find and represent equivalent names for fractions; use manipulatives to generate equivalent fractions.	**Goal 5.** Use numerical expressions to find and represent equivalent names for fractions and decimals; use and explain a multiplication rule to find equivalent fractions; rename fourths, fifths, tenths, and hundredths as decimals and percents.	**Goal 5.** Use numerical expressions to find and represent equivalent names for fractions, decimals, and percents; use and explain multiplication and division rules to find equivalent fractions and fractions in simplest form; convert between fractions and mixed numbers; convert between fractions, decimals, and percents.	**Goal 5.** Find equivalent fractions and fractions in simplest form by applying multiplication and division rules and concepts from number theory; convert between fractions, mixed numbers, decimals, and percents.

Program Goal: Understand Common Numerical Relations

Content	Kindergarten	First Grade	Second Grade	Third Grade	Fourth Grade	Fifth Grade	Sixth Grade
Comparing and ordering numbers	**Goal 6.** Compare and order whole numbers up to 20.	**Goal 7.** Compare and order whole numbers up to 1,000.	**Goal 7.** Compare and order whole numbers up to 10,000; use area models to compare fractions.	**Goal 6.** Compare and order whole numbers up to 1,000,000; use manipulatives to order decimals through hundredths; use area models and benchmark fractions to compare and order fractions.	**Goal 6.** Compare and order whole numbers up to 1,000,000,000 and decimals through thousandths; compare and order integers between −100 and 0; use area models, benchmark fractions, and analyses of numerators and denominators to compare and order fractions.	**Goal 6.** Compare and order rational numbers; use area models, benchmark fractions, and analyses of numerators and denominators to compare and order fractions and mixed numbers; describe strategies used to compare fractions and mixed numbers.	**Goal 6.** Choose and apply strategies for comparing and ordering rational numbers; explain those choices and strategies.

Everyday Mathematics

Content Strand: OPERATIONS AND COMPUTATION

Program Goal: Compute Accurately

Content	Kindergarten	First Grade	Second Grade	Third Grade	Fourth Grade	Fifth Grade	Sixth Grade
Addition and subtraction facts	Goal 1. Use manipulatives, number lines, and mental arithmetic to solve problems involving the addition and subtraction of single-digit whole numbers; demonstrate appropriate fluency with addition and subtraction facts within 5.	Goal 1. Demonstrate appropriate fluency with addition and subtraction facts through 10 + 10.	Goal 1. Demonstrate automaticity with all addition facts through 10 + 10 and fluency with the related subtraction facts.	Goal 1. Demonstrate automaticity with all addition and subtraction facts through 10 + 10; use basic facts to compute fact extensions such as 80 + 70.	Goal 1. Demonstrate automaticity with addition and subtraction fact extensions.		
Addition and subtraction procedures		Goal 2. Use manipulatives, number grids, tally marks, mental arithmetic, and calculators to solve problems involving the addition and subtraction of 1-digit whole numbers with 2-digit whole numbers; calculate and compare the values of combinations of coins.	Goal 2. Use manipulatives, number grids, tally marks, mental arithmetic, paper & pencil, and calculators to solve problems involving the addition and subtraction of multidigit whole numbers; describe the strategies used; calculate and compare values of coin and bill combinations.	Goal 2. Use manipulatives, mental arithmetic, paper-and-pencil algorithms and models, and calculators to solve problems involving the addition and subtraction of whole numbers and decimals in a money context; describe the strategies used and explain how they work.	Goal 2. Use manipulatives, mental arithmetic, paper-and-pencil algorithms and models, and calculators to solve problems involving the addition and subtraction of whole numbers and decimals through hundredths; describe the strategies used and explain how they work.	Goal 1. Use manipulatives, mental arithmetic, paper-and-pencil algorithms and models, and calculators to solve problems involving the addition and subtraction of whole numbers, decimals, and signed numbers; describe the strategies used and explain how they work.	Goal 1. Use mental arithmetic, paper-and-pencil algorithms and models, and calculators to solve problems involving the addition and subtraction of whole numbers, decimals, and signed numbers; describe the strategies used and explain how they work.

Everyday Mathematics

Content Strand: OPERATIONS AND COMPUTATION *cont.*

Program Goal: Compute Accurately *cont.*

Content	Kindergarten	First Grade	Second Grade	Third Grade	Fourth Grade	Fifth Grade	Sixth Grade
Multiplication and division facts				**Goal 3.** Demonstrate automaticity with multiplication facts through 10 × 10.	**Goal 3.** Demonstrate automaticity with multiplication facts through 10 * 10 and proficiency with related division facts; use basic facts to compute fact extensions such as 30 * 60.	**Goal 2.** Demonstrate automaticity with multiplication and division fact extensions.	
Multiplication and division procedures				**Goal 4.** Use arrays, mental arithmetic, paper-and-pencil algorithms and models, and calculators to solve problems involving the multiplication of 2- and 3-digit whole numbers by 1-digit whole numbers; describe the strategies used.	**Goal 4.** Use manipulatives, mental arithmetic, paper-and-pencil algorithms and models, and calculators to solve problems involving the multiplication of multidigit whole numbers by 2-digit whole numbers and the division of multidigit whole numbers by 1-digit whole numbers; describe the strategies used and explain how they work.	**Goal 3.** Use manipulatives, mental arithmetic, paper-and-pencil algorithms and models, and calculators to solve problems involving the multiplication of whole numbers and decimals and the division of multidigit whole numbers and decimals by whole numbers; express remainders as whole numbers or fractions as appropriate; describe the strategies used and explain how they work.	**Goal 2.** Use mental arithmetic, paper-and-pencil algorithms and models, and calculators to solve problems involving the multiplication and division of whole numbers, decimals, and signed numbers; describe the strategies used and explain how they work.

Everyday Mathematics

Content Strand: OPERATIONS AND COMPUTATION *cont.*

Program Goal: Compute Accurately *cont.*

Content	Kindergarten	First Grade	Second Grade	Third Grade	Fourth Grade	Fifth Grade	Sixth Grade
Procedures for addition and subtraction of fractions					**Goal 5.** Use manipulatives, mental arithmetic, and calculators to solve problems involving the addition and subtraction of fractions and mixed numbers; describe the strategies used.	**Goal 4.** Use mental arithmetic, paper-and-pencil algorithms and models, and calculators to solve problems involving the addition and subtraction of fractions and mixed numbers; describe the strategies used and explain how they work.	**Goal 3.** Use mental arithmetic, paper-and-pencil algorithms and models, and calculators to solve problems involving the addition and subtraction of fractions and mixed numbers; describe the strategies used and explain how they work.
Procedures for multiplication and division of fractions						**Goal 5.** Use area models, mental arithmetic, paper-and-pencil algorithms and models, and calculators to solve problems involving the multiplication of fractions and mixed numbers; use visual models, paper-and-pencil methods, and calculators to solve problems involving the division of fractions; describe the strategies used.	**Goal 4.** Use mental arithmetic, paper-and-pencil algorithms and models, and calculators to solve problems involving the multiplication and division of fractions and mixed numbers; describe the strategies used and explain how they work.

Everyday Mathematics

Content Strand: OPERATIONS AND COMPUTATION *cont.*

Program Goal: Make Reasonable Estimates

Content	Kindergarten	First Grade	Second Grade	Third Grade	Fourth Grade	Fifth Grade	Sixth Grade
Computational estimation		**Goal 3.** Estimate reasonableness of answers to basic fact problems (e.g., Will 7 + 8 be more or less than 10?).	**Goal 3.** Make reasonable estimates for whole number addition and subtraction problems; explain how the estimates were obtained.	**Goal 5.** Make reasonable estimates for whole number addition, subtraction, multiplication, and division problems; explain how the estimates were obtained.	**Goal 6.** Make reasonable estimates for whole number and decimal addition and subtraction problems and whole number multiplication and division problems; explain how the estimates were obtained.	**Goal 6.** Make reasonable estimates for whole number and decimal addition, subtraction, multiplication, and division problems and fraction and mixed number addition and subtraction problems; explain how the estimates were obtained.	**Goal 5.** Make reasonable estimates for whole number, decimal, fraction, and mixed number addition, subtraction, multiplication, and division problems; explain how the estimates were obtained.

Program Goal: Understand Meanings of Operations

Content	Kindergarten	First Grade	Second Grade	Third Grade	Fourth Grade	Fifth Grade	Sixth Grade
Models for the operations	**Goal 2.** Identify join and take-away situations.	**Goal 4.** Identify change-to-more, change-to-less, comparison, and parts-and-total situations.	**Goal 4.** Identify and describe change, comparison, and parts-and-total situations; use repeated addition, arrays, and skip counting to model multiplication; use equal sharing and equal grouping to model division.	**Goal 6.** Recognize and describe change, comparison, and parts-and-total situations; use repeated addition, arrays, and skip counting to model multiplication; use equal sharing and equal grouping to model division.	**Goal 7.** Use repeated addition, skip counting, arrays, area, and scaling to model multiplication and division.	**Goal 7.** Use repeated addition, arrays, area, and scaling to model multiplication and division; use ratios expressed as words, fractions, percents, and with colons; solve problems involving ratios of parts of a set to the whole set.	**Goal 6.** Use ratios and scaling to model size changes and to solve size-change problems; represent ratios as fractions, percents, and decimals, and using a colon; model and solve problems involving part-to-whole and part-to-part ratios; model rate and ratio number stories with proportions; use and explain cross multiplication and other strategies to solve proportions.

Everyday Mathematics

Content Strand: DATA AND CHANCE

Program Goal: Select and Create Appropriate Graphical Representations of Collected or Given Data

Content	Kindergarten	First Grade	Second Grade	Third Grade	Fourth Grade	Fifth Grade	Sixth Grade
Data collection and representation	**Goal 1.** Collect and organize data to create class-constructed tally charts, tables, and bar graphs.	**Goal 1.** Collect and organize data to create tally charts, tables, bar graphs, and line plots.	**Goal 1.** Collect and organize data or use given data to create tally charts, tables, graphs, and line plots.	**Goal 1.** Collect and organize data or use given data to create charts, tables, graphs, and line plots.	**Goal 1.** Collect and organize data or use given data to create charts, tables, graphs, and line plots.	**Goal 1.** Collect and organize data or use given data to create graphic displays with reasonable titles, labels, keys, and intervals.	**Goal 1.** Collect and organize data or use given data to create graphic displays with reasonable titles, labels, keys, and intervals.

Program Goal: Analyze and Interpret Data

Content	Kindergarten	First Grade	Second Grade	Third Grade	Fourth Grade	Fifth Grade	Sixth Grade
Data analysis	**Goal 2.** Use graphs to answer simple questions.	**Goal 2.** Use graphs to answer simple questions and draw conclusions; find the maximum and minimum of a data set.	**Goal 2.** Use graphs to ask and answer simple questions and draw conclusions; find the maximum, minimum, mode, and median of a data set.	**Goal 2.** Use graphs to ask and answer simple questions and draw conclusions; find the maximum, minimum, range, mode, and median of a data set.	**Goal 2.** Use the maximum, minimum, range, median, mode, and graphs to ask and answer questions, draw conclusions, and make predictions.	**Goal 2.** Use the maximum, minimum, range, median, mode, and mean and graphs to ask and answer questions, draw conclusions, and make predictions.	**Goal 2.** Use data landmarks, measures of spread, and graphs to ask and answer questions, draw conclusions, and make predictions; compare and contrast the median and mean of a data set.

Program Goal: Understand and Apply Basic Concepts of Probability

Content	Kindergarten	First Grade	Second Grade	Third Grade	Fourth Grade	Fifth Grade	Sixth Grade
Qualitative probability	**Goal 3.** Describe events using *certain, possible, impossible,* and other basic probability terms.	**Goal 3.** Describe events using *certain, likely, unlikely, impossible,* and other basic probability terms.	**Goal 3.** Describe events using *certain, likely, unlikely, impossible,* and other basic probability terms; explain the choice of language.	**Goal 3.** Describe events using *certain, very likely, likely, unlikely, very unlikely, impossible,* and other basic probability terms; explain the choice of language.	**Goal 3.** Describe events using *certain, very likely, likely, unlikely, very unlikely, impossible,* and other basic probability terms; use *more likely, equally likely, same chance, 50–50, less likely,* and other basic probability terms to compare events; explain the choice of language.	**Goal 3.** Describe events using *certain, very likely, likely, unlikely, very unlikely, impossible,* and other basic probability terms; use *more likely, equally likely, same chance, 50–50, less likely,* and other basic probability terms to compare events; explain the choice of language.	

Everyday Mathematics

Content Strand: DATA AND CHANCE *cont.*

Program Goal: Understand and Apply Basic Concepts of Probability *cont.*

Content	Kindergarten	First Grade	Second Grade	Third Grade	Fourth Grade	Fifth Grade	Sixth Grade
Quantitative probability				**Goal 4.** Predict the outcomes of simple experiments and test the predictions using manipulatives; express the probability of an event by using "__ out of __" language.	**Goal 4.** Predict the outcomes of experiments and test the predictions using manipulatives; summarize the results and use them to predict future events; express the probability of an event as a fraction.	**Goal 4.** Predict the outcomes of experiments, test the predictions using manipulatives, and summarize the results; compare predictions based on theoretical probability with experimental results; use summaries and comparisons to predict future events; express the probability of an event as a fraction, decimal, or percent.	**Goal 3.** Use the Multiplication Counting Principle, tree diagrams, and other counting strategies to identify all possible outcomes for a situation; predict results of experiments, test the predictions using manipulatives, and summarize the findings; compare predictions based on theoretical probability with experimental results; calculate probabilities and express them as fractions, decimals, and percents; explain how sample size affects results; use the results to predict future events.

Everyday Mathematics

Content Strand: MEASUREMENT AND REFERENCE FRAMES

Program Goal: Understand the Systems and Processes of Measurement; Use Appropriate Techniques, Tools, Units, and Formulas in Making Measurements

Content	Kindergarten	First Grade	Second Grade	Third Grade	Fourth Grade	Fifth Grade	Sixth Grade
Length, weight, and angles	**Goal 1.** Use nonstandard tools and techniques to estimate and compare weight and length; identify standard measuring tools.	**Goal 1.** Use nonstandard tools and techniques to estimate and compare weight and length; measure length with standard measuring tools.	**Goal 1.** Estimate length with and without tools; measure length to the nearest inch and centimeter; use standard and nonstandard tools to measure and estimate weight.	**Goal 1.** Estimate length with and without tools; measure length to the nearest $\frac{1}{2}$ inch and $\frac{1}{2}$ centimeter; draw and describe angles as records of rotations.	**Goal 1.** Estimate length with and without tools; measure length to the nearest $\frac{1}{4}$ inch and $\frac{1}{2}$ centimeter; use tools to measure and draw angles; estimate the size of angles without tools.	**Goal 1.** Estimate length with and without tools; measure length with tools to the nearest $\frac{1}{8}$ inch and millimeter; estimate the measure of angles with and without tools; use tools to draw angles with given measures.	**Goal 1.** Estimate length with and without tools; measure length with tools to the nearest $\frac{1}{16}$ inch and millimeter; estimate the measure of angles with and without tools; use tools to draw angles with given measures.
Area, perimeter, volume, and capacity			**Goal 2.** Partition rectangles into unit squares and count unit squares to find areas.	**Goal 2.** Describe and use strategies to measure the perimeter of polygons; find the areas of rectangles.	**Goal 2.** Describe and use strategies to measure the perimeter and area of polygons, to estimate the area of irregular shapes, and to find the volume of rectangular prisms.	**Goal 2.** Describe and use strategies to find the perimeter of polygons and the area of circles; choose and use appropriate methods, including formulas, to find the areas of rectangles, parallelograms, and triangles, and the volume of a prism; define *pi* as the ratio of a circle's circumference to its diameter.	**Goal 2.** Choose and use appropriate formulas to calculate the circumference of circles and to solve area, perimeter, and volume problems.
Units and systems of measurement			**Goal 3.** Describe relationships between days in a week and hours in a day.	**Goal 3.** Describe relationships among inches, feet, and yards; describe relationships between minutes in an hour, hours in a day, days in a week.	**Goal 3.** Describe relationships among U.S. customary units of measure and among metric units of measure.	**Goal 3.** Describe relationships among U.S. customary units of measure and among metric units of measure.	

Everyday Mathematics

Content Strand: MEASUREMENT AND REFERENCE FRAMES *cont.*

Program Goal: Understand the Systems and Processes of Measurement; Use Appropriate Techniques, Tools, Units, and Formulas in Making Measurements *cont.*

Content	Kindergarten	First Grade	Second Grade	Third Grade	Fourth Grade	Fifth Grade	Sixth Grade
Money	**Goal 2.** Identify pennies, nickels, dimes, quarters, and dollar bills.	**Goal 2.** Know and compare the value of pennies, nickels, dimes, quarters, and dollar bills; make exchanges between coins.	**Goal 4.** Make exchanges between coins and bills.				

Program Goal: Use and Understand Reference Frames

Content	Kindergarten	First Grade	Second Grade	Third Grade	Fourth Grade	Fifth Grade	Sixth Grade
Temperature	**Goal 3.** Describe temperature using appropriate vocabulary, such as *hot, warm,* and *cold;* identify a thermometer as a tool for measuring temperature.	**Goal 3.** Identify a thermometer as a tool for measuring temperature; read temperatures on Fahrenheit and Celsius thermometers to the nearest 10°.	**Goal 5.** Read temperature on both the Fahrenheit and Celsius scales.				
Time	**Goal 4.** Describe and use measures of time periods relative to a day and week; identify tools that measure time.	**Goal 4.** Use a calendar to identify days, weeks, months, and dates; tell and show time to the nearest half and quarter hour on an analog clock.	**Goal 6.** Tell and show time to the nearest five minutes on an analog clock; tell and write time in digital notation.	**Goal 4.** Tell and show time to the nearest minute on an analog clock; tell and write time in digital notation.			
Coordinate systems					**Goal 4.** Use ordered pairs of numbers to name, locate, and plot points in the first quadrant of a coordinate grid.	**Goal 4.** Use ordered pairs of numbers to name, locate, and plot points in all four quadrants of a coordinate grid.	**Goal 3.** Use ordered pairs of numbers to name, locate, and plot points in all four quadrants of a coordinate grid.

Everyday Mathematics

Program Goal: Investigate Characteristics and Properties of Two- and Three-Dimensional Geometric Shapes

Content	Kindergarten	First Grade	Second Grade	Third Grade	Fourth Grade	Fifth Grade	Sixth Grade
Lines and angles			**Goal 1.** Draw line segments and identify parallel line segments.	**Goal 1.** Identify and draw points, intersecting and parallel line segments and lines, rays, and right angles.	**Goal 1.** Identify, draw, and describe points, intersecting and parallel line segments and lines, rays, and right, acute, and obtuse angles.	**Goal 1.** Identify, describe, compare, name, and draw right, acute, obtuse, straight, and reflex angles; determine angle measures in vertical and supplementary angles and by applying properties of sums of angle measures in triangles and quadrangles.	**Goal 1.** Identify, describe, classify, name, and draw angles; determine angle measures by applying properties of orientations of angles and of sums of angle measures in triangles and quadrangles.
Plane and solid figures	**Goal 1.** Identify and describe plane and solid figures including circles, squares, triangles, rectangles, spheres, and cubes.	**Goal 1.** Identify and describe plane and solid figures including circles, triangles, squares, rectangles, spheres, cylinders, rectangular prisms, pyramids, cones, and cubes.	**Goal 2.** Identify, describe, and model plane and solid figures including circles, polygons, triangles, squares, rectangles, hexagons, trapezoids, rhombuses, spheres, cylinders, rectangular prisms, pyramids, cones, and cubes.	**Goal 2.** Identify, describe, model, and compare plane and solid figures including circles, polygons, spheres, cylinders, rectangular prisms, pyramids, cones, and cubes using appropriate geometric terms including the terms *face, edge, vertex, and base*.	**Goal 2.** Describe, compare, and classify plane and solid figures, including polygons, circles, spheres, cylinders, rectangular prisms, cones, cubes, and pyramids, using appropriate geometric terms including *vertex, base, face, edge, and congruent*.	**Goal 2.** Describe, compare, and classify plane and solid figures using appropriate geometric terms; identify congruent figures and describe their properties.	**Goal 2.** Identify and describe similar and congruent figures and describe their properties; construct a figure that is congruent to another figure using a compass and straightedge.

Program Goal: Apply Transformations and Symmetry in Geometric Situations

Content	Kindergarten	First Grade	Second Grade	Third Grade	Fourth Grade	Fifth Grade	Sixth Grade
Transformations and symmetry	**Goal 2.** Identify shapes having line symmetry.	**Goal 2.** Identify shapes having line symmetry; complete line-symmetric shapes or designs.	**Goal 3.** Create and complete two-dimensional symmetric shapes or designs.	**Goal 3.** Create and complete two-dimensional symmetric shapes or designs; locate multiple lines of symmetry in a two-dimensional shape.	**Goal 3.** Identify, describe, and sketch examples of reflections; identify and describe examples of translations and rotations.	**Goal 3.** Identify, describe, and sketch examples of reflections, translations, and rotations.	**Goal 3.** Identify, describe, and sketch (including plotting on the coordinate plane) instances of reflections, translations, and rotations.

Everyday Mathematics

Program Goal: Understand Patterns and Functions

Content	Kindergarten	First Grade	Second Grade	Third Grade	Fourth Grade	Fifth Grade	Sixth Grade
Patterns and functions	**Goal 1.** Extend, describe, and create visual, rhythmic, and movement patterns; use rules, which will lead to functions, to sort, make patterns, and play "What's My Rule?" and other games.	**Goal 1.** Extend, describe, and create numeric, visual, and concrete patterns; solve problems involving function machines, "What's My Rule?" tables, and Frames-and-Arrows diagrams.	**Goal 1.** Extend, describe, and create numeric, visual, and concrete patterns; describe rules for patterns and use them to solve problems; use words and symbols to describe and write rules for functions involving addition and subtraction and use those rules to solve problems.	**Goal 1.** Extend, describe, and create numeric patterns; describe rules for patterns and use them to solve problems; use words and symbols to describe and write rules for functions involving addition, subtraction, multiplication and use those rules to solve problems.	**Goal 1.** Extend, describe, and create numeric patterns; describe rules for patterns and use them to solve problems; use words and symbols to describe and write rules for functions that involve the four basic arithmetic operations and use those rules to solve problems.	**Goal 1.** Extend, describe, and create numeric patterns; describe rules for patterns and use them to solve problems; write rules for functions involving the four basic arithmetic operations; represent functions using words, symbols, tables, and graphs and use those representations to solve problems.	**Goal 1.** Extend, describe, and create numeric patterns; describe rules for patterns and use them to solve problems; represent patterns and rules using algebraic notation; represent functions using words, algebraic notation, tables, and graphs; translate from one representation to another and use representations to solve problems involving functions.

Program Goal: Use Algebraic Notation to Represent and Analyze Situations and Structures

Content	Kindergarten	First Grade	Second Grade	Third Grade	Fourth Grade	Fifth Grade	Sixth Grade
Algebraic notation and solving number sentences	**Goal 2.** Read and write expressions and number sentences using the symbols $+$, $-$, and $=$.	**Goal 2.** Read, write, and explain expressions and number sentences using the symbols $+$, $-$, and $=$ and the symbols $>$ and $<$ with cues; solve equations involving addition and subtraction.	**Goal 2.** Read, write, and explain expressions and number sentences using the symbols $+$, $-$, $=$, $>$, and $<$; solve number sentences involving addition and subtraction; write expressions and number sentences to model number stories.	**Goal 2.** Read, write, and explain number sentences using the symbols $+$, $-$, $\times$, $\div$, $=$, $>$, and $<$; solve number sentences; write expressions and number sentences to model number stories.	**Goal 2.** Use conventional notation to write expressions and number sentences using the four basic arithmetic operations; determine whether number sentences are true or false; solve open sentences and explain the solutions; write expressions and number sentences to model number stories.	**Goal 2.** Determine whether number sentences are true or false; solve open number sentences and explain the solutions; use a letter variable to write an open sentence to model a number story; use a pan-balance model to solve linear equations in one unknown.	**Goal 2.** Determine whether equalities and inequalities are true or false; solve open number sentences and explain the solutions; use a pan-balance model to solve linear equations in one or two unknowns; use trial-and-error and equivalent equations strategies to solve linear equations in one unknown.

Everyday Mathematics

Content Strand: PATTERNS, FUNCTIONS, AND ALGEBRA *cont.*

Program Goal: Use Algebraic Notation to Represent and Analyze Situations and Structures *cont.*

Content	Kindergarten	First Grade	Second Grade	Third Grade	Fourth Grade	Fifth Grade	Sixth Grade
Order of operations				**Goal 3.** Recognize that numeric expressions can have different values depending on the order in which operations are carried out; understand that grouping symbols can be used to affect the order in which operations are carried out.	**Goal 3.** Evaluate numeric expressions containing grouping symbols; insert grouping symbols to make number sentences true.	**Goal 3.** Evaluate numeric expressions containing grouping symbols and nested grouping symbols; insert grouping symbols and nested grouping symbols to make number sentences true; describe and use the precedence of multiplication and division over addition and subtraction.	**Goal 3.** Describe and apply the conventional order of operations.
Properties of the arithmetic operations		**Goal 3.** Apply the Commutative and Associative Properties of Addition and the Additive Identity to basic addition fact problems.	**Goal 3.** Describe the Commutative and Associative Properties of Addition and the Additive Identity and apply them to mental arithmetic problems.	**Goal 4.** Describe and apply the Commutative and Associative Properties of Addition and Multiplication and the Multiplicative Identity; apply the Distributive Property of Multiplication over Addition.	**Goal 4.** Describe and apply the Distributive Property of Multiplication over Addition.	**Goal 4.** Describe and apply properties of arithmetic.	**Goal 4.** Describe and apply properties of arithmetic and multiplicative and additive inverses.

Assessment Overviews

This section summarizes the assessment opportunities in each unit. Ongoing assessments, such as the Informing Instruction and Recognizing Student Achievement notes, are listed by lesson. Portfolio opportunities, paired or linked Math Boxes, and Writing/Reasoning prompts are also highlighted. You will find information on periodic assessments as well. Modifications for each unit's Progress Check Written Assessment, tips for implementing Open Response tasks (including rubrics for each task), and sample student responses for each rubric level are provided.

Contents

Beginning-of-Year Assessment Goals

The Beginning-of-Year Assessment (pages 222A–222C) can be used to gauge children's readiness for the content they will encounter early in second grade. This allows you to plan your instruction accordingly. The following table provides the goals for all the problems in the Beginning-of-Year Assessment.

Problem(s)	Grade-Level Goal
1	**Number and Numeration 2:** Read, write, and model with manipulatives whole numbers up to 10,000; identify places in such numbers and the values of the digits in those places; read and write money amounts in dollars-and-cents notation.
2	**Number and Numeration 5:** Use tally marks, arrays, and numerical expressions involving addition and subtraction to give equivalent names for whole numbers.
3a–3f	**Operations and Computation 1:** Demonstrate automaticity with all addition facts through 10 + 10 and fluency with the related subtraction facts.
3g–3j	**Patterns, Functions, and Algebra 3:** Describe the Commutative and Associative Properties of Addition and the Additive Identity and apply them to mental arithmetic problems.
4	**Measurement and Reference Frames 6:** Tell and show time to the nearest five minutes on an analog clock; tell and write time in digital notation.
5	**Patterns, Functions, and Algebra 1:** Extend, describe, and create numeric, visual, and concrete patterns; describe rules for patterns and use them to solve problems; use words and symbols to describe and write rules for functions involving addition and subtraction and use those rules to solve problems.
6	**Data and Chance 2:** Use graphs to ask and answer simple questions and draw conclusions; find the maximum, minimum, mode, and median of a data set.
7	**Operations and Computation 2:** Use manipulatives, number grids, tally marks, mental arithmetic, paper & pencil, and calculators to solve problems involving the addition and subtraction of multidigit whole numbers; describe the strategies used; calculate and compare values of coin and bill combinations.
8	**Measurement and Reference Frames 4:** Make exchanges between coins and bills.

Assessment Overview

In this unit, children are introduced to a variety of routines that provide them with opportunities to explore, compare, and order numbers, as well as to work with number sequences and patterns. Use the information in this section to develop your assessment plan for Unit 1.

Ongoing Assessment

Opportunities for using and collecting ongoing assessment information are highlighted in Informing Instruction and Recognizing Student Achievement notes. Student products, along with observations and suggested writing prompts, provide a range of useful assessment information.

Informing Instruction

The Informing Instruction notes highlight children's thinking and point out common misconceptions. Informing Instruction in Unit 1: Lessons 1-1, 1-3, 1-5, 1-6, 1-7, and 1-11.

Recognizing Student Achievement

The Recognizing Student Achievement notes highlight specific tasks from which teachers can collect assessment data to monitor and document children's progress toward meeting Grade-Level Goals.

Lesson	Content Assessed	Where to Find It
1◆1	**Write and order numbers.** [Number and Numeration Goal 7]	*TLG*, p. 21
1◆2	**Count coin combinations.** [Operations and Computation Goal 2]	*TLG*, p. 26
1◆3	**Tell time to the nearest half-hour.** [Measurement and Reference Frames Goal 6]	*TLG*, p. 31
1◆4	**Know basic addition facts.** [Operations and Computation Goal 1]	*TLG*, p. 36
1◆5	**Count bill combinations.** [Operations and Computation Goal 2]	*TLG*, p. 39
1◆6	**Solve sum-equals-ten facts.** [Operations and Computation Goal 1]	*TLG*, p. 45
1◆7	**Complete and describe a number pattern.** [Patterns, Functions, and Algebra Goal 1]	*TLG*, p. 47
1◆8	**Solve number-grid puzzles using number-grid patterns.** [Patterns, Functions, and Algebra Goal 1]	*TLG*, p. 53
1◆9	**Use number models to write equivalent names for numbers.** [Number and Numeration Goal 5]	*TLG*, p. 58
1◆10	**Calculate the values of coin combinations.** [Operations and Computation Goal 2]	*TLG*, p. 63
1◆11	**Compare numbers.** [Number and Numeration Goal 7]	*TLG*, p. 66
1◆12	**Identify odd and even numbers.** [Number and Numeration Goal 4]	*TLG*, p. 75

Math Boxes

Math Boxes, one of several types of tasks highlighted in the Recognizing Student Achievement notes, have an additional useful feature. Math Boxes in most lessons are paired or linked with Math Boxes in one or two other lessons that have similar problems. Paired or linked Math Boxes in Unit 1: 1-7, 1-9, and 1-11; and 1-8, 1-10, and 1-12.

Writing/Reasoning Prompts

In Unit 1, a variety of writing prompts encourage children to explain their strategies and thinking, to reflect on their learning, and to make connections to other mathematics or life experiences. Here are some of the Unit 1 suggestions:

Lesson	Writing/Reasoning Prompts	Where to Find It
1♦7	Explain your strategies for finding the missing numbers on the number grid.	*TLG*, p. 49
1♦10	Explain how you found the fewest number of coins.	*TLG*, p. 63
1♦12	Explain how you know whether 15 is an odd number or an even number.	*TLG*, p. 74

Portfolio Opportunities

Portfolios are a versatile tool for assessment. They help children reflect on their mathematical growth and help teachers understand and document that growth. Each unit identifies several student products that can be selected and stored in a portfolio. Here are some of the Unit 1 suggestions:

Lesson	Portfolio Opportunities	Where to Find It
1♦7	Children find missing numbers on number grids.	*TLG*, p. 49
1♦10	Children explain how they found the fewest number of coins to show an amount.	*TLG*, p. 63
1♦12	Children explain how they know whether a number is odd or even.	*TLG*, p. 74

Periodic Assessment

Every Progress Check lesson includes opportunities to observe children's progress and to collect student products in a variety of ways—Self Assessment, Oral and Slate Assessment, Written Assessment, and an Open Response task. For more details, see the first page of Progress Check 1, Lesson 1-13 on page 76, of the *Teacher's Lesson Guide*.

Progress Check Modifications

Written Assessments are one way children demonstrate what they know. The table below shows modifications for the Written Assessment in this unit. Use these to maximize opportunities for children to demonstrate what they know. Modifications can be given individually or written on the board for the class.

Problem(s)	Modifications for Written Assessment
1	For Problem 1, use craft sticks to model tallies.
2	For Problem 2, write the value of each coin above the picture of the coin.
6	For Problem 6, describe patterns you can use to fill in the missing numbers in the number grid.
11	For Problem 11, use a number grid to solve the problem.

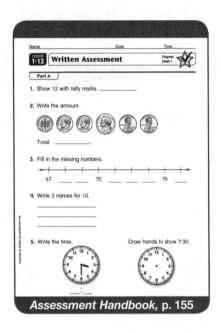

Assessment Handbook, p. 155

The Written Assessment for the Unit 1 Progress Check is on pages 155–156.

Open Response, *Locker Numbers*

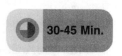

Description

For this task, children solve a number-grid puzzle and find patterns.

Focus

- ◆ **Count on and back using a number grid.**
  [Number and Numeration Goal 1]
- ◆ **Describe patterns and use patterns to solve problems.**
  [Patterns, Functions, and Algebra Goal 1]

Implementation Tips

- ◆ Allow children to share their ideas verbally before recording in words.
- ◆ Have children underline or circle the word *describe* in the last part of the problem to remind them to explain their thinking.

Assessment Handbook, p. 157

Modifications for Meeting Diverse Needs

- ◆ Have children extend the number grid before solving the problem.
- ◆ Have children look at the illustration of the lockers and describe how it is the same and how it is different from the 100-grid. Have them write an addition or subtraction problem that they could solve using the lockers. Have children explain in words how they would use the locker illustration.

Improving Open Response Skills

After children complete the task, record and share some of the explanations for the patterns they found in the locker numbers. For each pattern they describe, have children try to determine what is shaded based on the description. Have children identify the essential information. If the description does not give enough information to determine what is shaded, have children describe information that is missing.

Note: The wording and formatting of the text on the student samples that follow may vary slightly from the actual task your children will complete. These minor discrepancies will not affect the implementation of the task.

Rubric

This rubric is designed to help you assess levels of mathematical performance on this task. It emphasizes mathematical understanding with only a mention of clarity of explanation. Consider the expectations of standardized tests in your area when applying a rubric. Modify this sample rubric as appropriate.

4	Completes the grid and clearly explains the strategy used to fill in the missing numbers. Identifies, shades, and describes a pattern that involves relationships among the numbers in the grid. Uses mathematical words or symbols in the description of the pattern, such as *before, after, next, decreases, increases, counting by,* or *+1.*
3	Completes the grid and explains the strategy used, but the explanation might be incomplete. Identifies, shades, and describes a pattern, but might not use mathematical words or symbols. The description might not exactly explain the pattern.
2	Attempts to complete the grid, but the explanation shows no evidence of a strategy used. Might shade a pattern, but the description is missing, unclear, or does not match what is shaded.
1	Might attempt to complete the grid. Might attempt an explanation, but there is no evidence of an understanding of patterns in the grid. Might attempt to shade a pattern, but the description is unclear or missing.
0	Does not attempt to understand or solve the problem.

Sample Student Responses

This Level 4 paper illustrates the following features: The grid is completed. A counting-back strategy is used and clearly described with words and a number sentence. A pattern is shaded and described in words and with numbers. The description explains that the ones-digit decreases when moving down a column.

This Level 4 paper illustrates the following features: The grid is completed. A counting-back strategy is used and described in words. A pattern is shaded and described with a Frames-and-Arrows diagram. The diagram illustrates that the numbers increase by 10 along one diagonal.

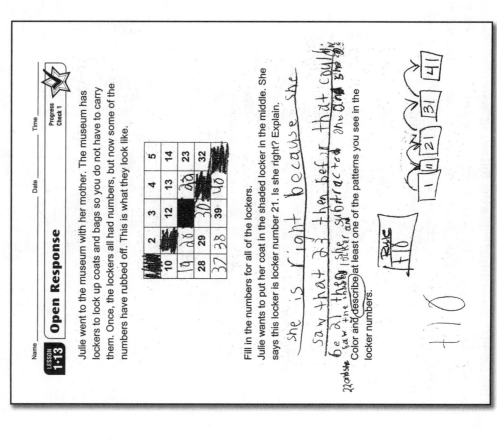

Julie went to the museum with her mother. The museum has lockers to lock up coats and bags so you do not have to carry them. Once, the lockers all had numbers, but now some of the numbers have rubbed off. This is what they look like.

1	2	3	4	5
10		12	13	14
19	20		21	23
28	29		30	32
37	38	39	40	

Fill in the numbers for all of the lockers.

Julie wants to put her coat in the shaded locker in the middle. She says this locker is locker number 21. Is she right? Explain.

she is right because she saw that 23 then befor that coul be all three. she saw the inside, subtracted she one she 20

Color and describe at least one of the patterns you see in the locker numbers.

[Frames-and-Arrows diagram: 1, 11, 21, 31, 41]

Out

Julie went to the museum with her mother. The museum has lockers to lock up coats and bags so you do not have to carry them. Once, the lockers all had numbers, but now some of the numbers have rubbed off. This is what they look like.

1	2	3	4	5
10	11	12	13	14
19	20	21	22	23
28	29	30	31	32
37	38	39	40	41

Fill in the numbers for all of the lockers.

Julie wants to put her coat in the shaded locker in the middle. She says this locker is locker number 21. Is she right? Explain.

Yes. Because 23−2=21, and that is what the number in the middle is I think.

Color and describe at least one of the patterns you see in the locker numbers.

I chose the second-to-last going down pattern. The pattern is, If you go down, the number decreases. 4,3,2,1,0

2U01L13M05

This Level 3 paper illustrates the following features: The grid is completed. A counting-back strategy is used and described with words. A pattern is shaded and described in words and numbers, but the description does not exactly explain the shaded pattern. There is a minor error in the number sequence listed.

This Level 3 paper illustrates the following features: The grid is completed. A strategy of using the pattern on the diagonal is used. The description of the strategy makes sense but is incomplete. A pattern is shaded and described in words and numbers. The description explains that the numbers increase by 10 along one diagonal.

Julie went to the museum with her mother. The museum has lockers to lock up coats and bags so you do not have to carry them. Once, the lockers all had numbers, but now some of the numbers have rubbed off. This is what they look like.

2	3	4	5
10	12	13	14
19	20	22	23
28	29	30	32
37	38	39	40

Fill in the numbers for all of the lockers.

Julie wants to put her coat in the shaded locker in the middle. She says this locker is locker number 21. Is she right? Explain.

yes Beause
going and ll are
going diagonaliy

Color and describe at least one of the patterns you see in the locker numbers.

diagnal pattern

0+10 12 14 44 pattern

Julie went to the museum with her mother. The museum has lockers to lock up coats and bags so you do not have to carry them. Once, the lockers all had numbers, but now some of the numbers have rubbed off. This is what they look like.

2	3	4	5
10	12	13	14
19	20	22	23
28	29	30	32
37	38	39	40

Fill in the numbers for all of the lockers.

Julie wants to put her coat in the shaded locker in the middle. She says this locker is locker number 21. Is she right? Explain.

Julie is right Because I started
from 23 and went back 2 to get 21.

Color and describe at least one of the patterns you see in the locker numbers.

110 21 31 41

I chose This pattern Because They
all had 1 in Them

This Level 2 paper illustrates the following features: The grid is completed, but the explanation does not clearly indicate a strategy. A pattern is shaded and described in words, but the description does not explain the shaded pattern.

LESSON 1·13

Open Response

Progress Check 1

Julie went to the museum with her mother. The museum has lockers to lock up coats and bags so you do not have to carry them. Once, the lockers all had numbers, but now some of the numbers have rubbed off. This is what they look like.

1	2	3	4
10	11	12	13
19	20	22	
28	29	30	31
37	38	39	40

Fill in the numbers for all of the lockers.

Julie wants to put her coat in the shaded locker in the middle. She says this locker is locker number 21. Is she right? Explain.

Yes. Because it you concentrate on one rectangle, your going by one's.

Color and describe at least one of the patterns you see in the locker numbers. If you look down a rectangle it's counting by eleven.

This Level 1 paper illustrates the following features: There is an attempt to complete the grid, but the explanation does not indicate a strategy. No pattern is shaded. There is an attempt at an explanation, but it does not make sense in the context of the problem.

LESSON 1·13

Open Response

Progress Check 1

Julie went to the museum with her mother. The museum has lockers to lock up coats and bags so you do not have to carry them. Once, the lockers all had numbers, but now some of the numbers have rubbed off. This is what they look like.

1	2	3	4	5
10	11	12	13	14
15	16	21	23	
28	29	30	31	32
32	33	39	40	41

Fill in the numbers for all of the lockers.

Julie wants to put her coat in the shaded locker in the middle. She says this locker is locker number 21. Is she right? Explain.

Yes 21 She White on the locker.

Color and describe at least one of the patterns you see in the locker numbers. I see 2 in a pattern.

Assessment Overview

In this unit, children focus on building fact power for basic addition and subtraction facts, and apply their fact work in a series of routines involving patterns and functions. Use the information in this section to develop your assessment plan for Unit 2.

Ongoing Assessment

Opportunities for using and collecting ongoing assessment information are highlighted in Informing Instruction and Recognizing Student Achievement notes. Student products, along with observations and suggested writing prompts, provide a range of useful assessment information.

Informing Instruction

The Informing Instruction notes highlight children's thinking and point out common misconceptions. Informing Instruction in Unit 2: Lessons 2-1, 2-2, 2-3, and 2-8.

Recognizing Student Achievement

The Recognizing Student Achievement notes highlight specific tasks from which teachers can collect assessment data to monitor and document children's progress toward meeting Grade-Level Goals.

Lesson	Content Assessed	Where to Find It
2•1	**Write a number story.** [Operations and Computation Goal 4]	*TLG*, p. 97
2•2	**Recall math facts more quickly than a calculator.** [Operations and Computation Goal 1]	*TLG*, p. 102
2•3	**Count back by 5s.** [Number and Numeration Goal 1]	*TLG*, p. 109
2•4	**Recall math facts more quickly than a calculator.** [Operations and Computation Goal 1]	*TLG*, p. 114
2•5	**Know doubles facts.** [Operations and Computation Goal 1]	*TLG*, p. 117
2•6	**Write fact families for dominoes.** [Patterns, Functions, and Algebra Goal 3]	*TLG*, p. 124
2•7	**Write a number story to describe a number sentence.** [Patterns, Functions, and Algebra Goal 2]	*TLG*, p. 129
2•8	**Use counting patterns on the number grid.** [Patterns, Functions, and Algebra Goal 1]	*TLG*, p. 133
2•9	**Write number sentences and generate equivalent names for a given number.** [Number and Numeration Goal 5]	*TLG*, p. 140
2•10	**Extend a numeric pattern using addition and subtraction.** [Patterns, Functions, and Algebra Goal 1]	*TLG*, p. 146
2•11	**Solve "What's My Rule?" problems using addition and subtraction with a known rule.** [Patterns, Functions, and Algebra Goal 1]	*TLG*, p. 152
2•12	**Write a fact family from a Fact Triangle.** [Operations and Computation Goal 1]	*TLG*, p. 159
2•13	**Write a number story for a number model.** [Patterns, Functions, and Algebra Goal 2]	*TLG*, p. 162

Math Boxes

Math Boxes, one of several types of tasks highlighted in the Recognizing Student Achievement notes, have an additional useful feature. Math Boxes in most lessons are paired or linked with Math Boxes in one or two other lessons that have similar problems. Paired or linked Math Boxes in Unit 2: 2-1 and 2-3; 2-2 and 2-4; 2-5 and 2-7; 2-6 and 2-8; 2-9, 2-11, and 2-13; and 2-10 and 2-12.

Writing/Reasoning Prompts

In Unit 2, a variety of writing prompts encourage children to explain their strategies and thinking, to reflect on their learning, and to make connections to other mathematics or life experiences. Here are some of the Unit 2 suggestions:

Lesson	Writing/Reasoning Prompts	Where to Find It
2◆4	Explain how you used your calculator to find the answers.	*TLG*, p. 114
2◆7	Explain how writing two addition facts helps you write two subtraction facts.	*TLG*, p. 129
2◆11	Explain what coins you would use to pay $1.50 with the fewest coins possible.	*TLG*, p. 153
2◆12	Explain how a doubles fact helps you solve other problems.	*TLG*, p. 158

Portfolio Opportunities

Portfolios are a versatile tool for assessment. They help children reflect on their mathematical growth and help teachers understand and document that growth. Each unit identifies several student products that can be selected and stored in a portfolio. Here are some of the Unit 2 suggestions:

Lesson	Portfolio Opportunities	Where to Find It
2◆3	Children explain how they found the missing number.	*TLG*, p. 109
2◆5	Children record at least 5 of the 10 double facts.	*TLG*, p. 117
2◆5	Children make a Doubles Facts Book.	*TLG*, p. 120
2◆8	Children describe patterns they see in the number grid.	*TLG*, p. 136

Periodic Assessment

Every Progress Check lesson includes opportunities to observe children's progress and to collect student products in a variety of ways—Self Assessment, Oral and Slate Assessment, Written Assessment, and an Open Response task. For more details, see the first page of Progress Check 2, Lesson 2-14 on page 166, of the *Teacher's Lesson Guide*.

Progress Check Modifications

Written Assessments are one way children demonstrate what they know. The table below shows modifications for the Written Assessment in this unit. Use these to maximize opportunities for children to demonstrate what they know. Modifications can be given individually or written on the board for the class.

Problem(s)	Modifications for Written Assessment
3, 4	For Problems 3 and 4, use counters to help you solve the problem.
5, 6	For Problems 5 and 6, use a number line or number grid to help you solve the problems.
7	For Problem 7, explain how you could use a calculator to find each of the missing numbers.
12	For Problem 12, record a number model to show how you found the total.

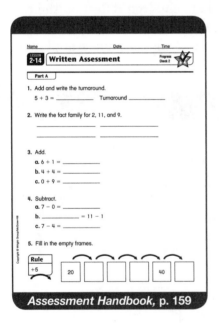

Assessment Handbook, p. 159

The Written Assessment for the Unit 2 Progress Check is on pages 159–161.

Open Response, *Train Boxes*

 45-60 Min.

Description

For this task, children identify and use patterns to solve a number story.

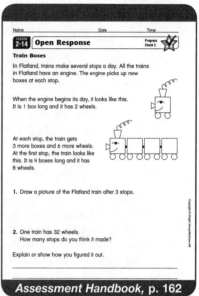

Assessment Handbook, p. 162

Focus

◆ **Skip count forward by twos.**
  [Number and Numeration Goal 1]

◆ **Extend, describe, and use numeric patterns to solve problems.**
  [Patterns, Functions, and Algebra Goal 1]

Implementation Tips

◆ Provide children with counters.

◆ Encourage children to keep track of each stop in their drawings.

Modifications for Meeting Diverse Needs

◆ Take a number of sheets of plain white paper and cut each sheet into four equal pieces. Have children draw the engine on one piece and each stop on a separate piece. They can then manipulate the papers to build the train and determine the number of wheels at a given stop.

◆ Start by having children solve the problem without drawing a picture. Ask them to write a number sentence they could use to help solve the problem. Have children use the pattern to extend their work to the tenth stop.

Improving Open Response Skills

After children complete the task, have them model a variety of explanations or create illustrations for how they solved the problem. Have children compare the explanations and illustrations. Ask: *Which ones are similar, and how? How do the explanations differ? What is needed in an explanation or illustration for it to be complete?*

Note: The wording and formatting of the text on the student samples that follow may vary slightly from the actual task your children will complete. These minor discrepancies will not affect the implementation of the task.

Rubric

This rubric is designed to help you assess levels of mathematical performance on this task. It emphasizes mathematical understanding with only a mention of clarity of explanation. Consider the expectations of standardized tests in your area when applying a rubric. Modify this sample rubric as appropriate.

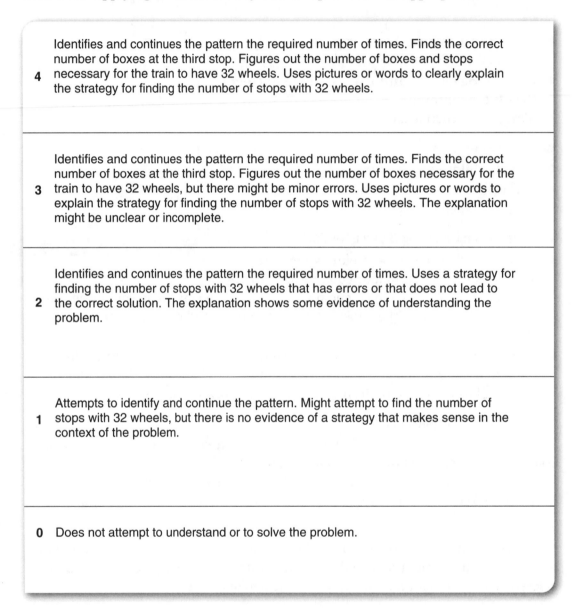

4 Identifies and continues the pattern the required number of times. Finds the correct number of boxes at the third stop. Figures out the number of boxes and stops necessary for the train to have 32 wheels. Uses pictures or words to clearly explain the strategy for finding the number of stops with 32 wheels.

3 Identifies and continues the pattern the required number of times. Finds the correct number of boxes at the third stop. Figures out the number of boxes necessary for the train to have 32 wheels, but there might be minor errors. Uses pictures or words to explain the strategy for finding the number of stops with 32 wheels. The explanation might be unclear or incomplete.

2 Identifies and continues the pattern the required number of times. Uses a strategy for finding the number of stops with 32 wheels that has errors or that does not lead to the correct solution. The explanation shows some evidence of understanding the problem.

1 Attempts to identify and continue the pattern. Might attempt to find the number of stops with 32 wheels, but there is no evidence of a strategy that makes sense in the context of the problem.

0 Does not attempt to understand or to solve the problem.

Sample Student Responses

This Level 4 paper illustrates the following features: The pattern is continued the required number of times for each part of the problem. The explanation clearly describes the use of dividing 15 into groups of three to find the number of stops.

This Level 4 paper illustrates the following features: The pattern is continued the required number of times for each part of the problem. The illustration clearly shows the use of repeated groups of three cars to find the number of stops.

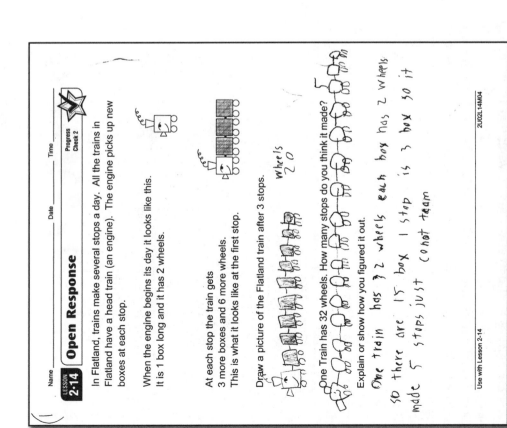

Name _____ Date _____ Time _____

LESSON 2·14

Open Response

Progress Check 2

In Flatland, trains make several stops a day. All the trains in Flatland have a head train (an engine). The engine picks up new boxes at each stop.

When the engine begins its day it looks like this. It is 1 box long and it has 2 wheels.

At each stop the train gets 3 more boxes and 6 more wheels. This is what it looks like at the first stop.

Draw a picture of the Flatland train after 3 stops.

wheels 20

One Train has 32 wheels. How many stops do you think it made?

Explain or show how you figured it out.

One train has 32 wheels each boy has 2 wheels
so there are 15 box 1 stop is 3 box so it
made 5 stops just cohat team

Use with Lesson 2-14

2U02L14M04

Name _____ Date _____ Time _____

LESSON 2·14

Open Response

Progress Check 2

In Flatland, trains make several stops a day. All the trains in Flatland have a head train (an engine). The engine picks up new boxes at each stop.

When the engine begins its day it looks like this. It is 1 box long and it has 2 wheels.

At each stop the train gets 3 more boxes and 6 more wheels. This is what it looks like at the first stop.

Draw a picture of the Flatland train after 3 stops.

One Train has 32 wheels. How many stops do you think it made?

Explain or show how you figured it out.

Use with Lesson 2-14

2U02L14M04

This Level 3 paper illustrates the following features: The pattern three cars is continued the required number of times for each part of the problem. The illustration for how to find the number of stops demonstrates an understanding of the problem, but there is no clear answer or strategy suggested by the illustration.

LESSON
2·14   **Open Response**   Progress
                                            Check 2

In Flatland, trains make several stops a day. All the trains in Flatland have a head train (an engine). The engine picks up new boxes at each stop.

When the engine begins its day it looks like this. It is 1 box long and it has 2 wheels.

At each stop the train gets 3 more boxes and 6 more wheels. This is what it looks like at the first stop.

Draw a picture of the Flatland train after 3 stops.

One Train has 32 wheels. How many stops do you think it made?

Explain or show how you figured it out.

This Level 3 paper illustrates the following features: The pattern of three cars is continued the required number of times for 3 stops, and repeated many times for the number of stops for 32 wheels. The illustration of how the number of stops is found demonstrates an understanding of the problem, but there is no clear indication of how the answer was arrived at.

LESSON
2·14   **Open Response**   Progress
                                            Check 2

In Flatland, trains make several stops a day. All the trains in Flatland have a head train (an engine). The engine picks up new boxes at each stop.

When the engine begins its day it looks like this. It is 1 box long and it has 2 wheels.

At each stop the train gets 3 more boxes and 6 more wheels. This is what it looks like at the first stop.

Draw a picture of the Flatland train after 3 stops.

One Train has 32 wheels. How many stops do you think it made?

Explain or show how you figured it out.

This Level 2 paper illustrates the following features: The pattern of three cars is continued the required number of times for 3 stops and repeated many times for the number of stops with 32 wheels. The illustration for finding the number of stops demonstrates some understanding of the problem. The answer given is incorrect, and no strategy is explained.

This Level 1 paper illustrates the following features: The pattern of three cars is continued the required number of times for 3 stops. There is no evidence of understanding the pattern in the illustration for finding the number of stops. The answer given is correct, but no strategy is explained or illustrated.

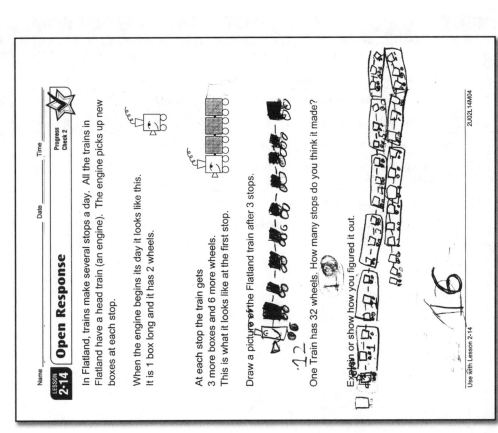

Assessment Overview

In this unit, children continue to explore place value, make coin combinations, and tell time. Use the information in this section to develop your assessment plan for Unit 3.

Ongoing Assessment

Opportunities for using and collecting ongoing assessment information are highlighted in Informing Instruction and Recognizing Student Achievement notes. Student products, along with observations and suggested writing prompts, provide a range of useful assessment information.

Informing Instruction
The Informing Instruction notes highlight children's thinking and point out common misconceptions. Informing Instruction in Unit 3: Lessons 3-1, 3-3, 3-5, and 3-6.

Recognizing Student Achievement
The Recognizing Student Achievement notes highlight specific tasks from which teachers can collect assessment data to monitor and document children's progress toward meeting Grade-Level Goals.

Lesson	Content Assessed	Where to Find It
3·1	**Write numbers shown with base-10 blocks.** [Number and Numeration Goal 2]	*TLG,* p. 187
3·2	**Show coin combinations.** [Operations and Computation Goal 2]	*TLG,* p. 193
3·3	**Record tally marks for a given number.** [Number and Numeration Goal 5]	*TLG,* p. 197
3·4	**Show time to the nearest half-hour.** [Measurement and Reference Frames Goal 6]	*TLG,* p. 206
3·5	**Show equivalent names for 20.** [Number and Numeration Goal 5]	*TLG,* p. 211
3·6	**Create number patterns and rules in Frames-and-Arrows problems.** [Patterns, Functions, and Algebra Goal 1]	*TLG,* p. 216
3·7	**Make the largest number from two digits.** [Number and Numeration Goal 2]	*TLG,* p. 222
3·8	**Calculate the value of coin combinations.** [Operations and Computation Goal 2]	*TLG,* p. 227

Math Boxes

Math Boxes, one of several types of tasks highlighted in the Recognizing Student Achievement notes, have an additional useful feature. Math Boxes in most lessons are paired or linked with Math Boxes in one or two other lessons that have similar problems. Paired or linked Math Boxes in Unit 3: 3-1 and 3-3; 3-2 and 3-4; and 3-5 and 3-7.

Writing/Reasoning Prompts

In Unit 3, a variety of writing prompts encourage children to explain their strategies and thinking, to reflect on their learning, and to make connections to other mathematics or life experiences. Here are some of the Unit 3 suggestions:

Lesson	Writing/Reasoning Prompts	Where to Find It
3•3	Explain how you found the answers to extended fact problems.	*TLG*, p. 200
3•4	Explain how you found how many more points Room 106 scored than Room 104.	*TLG*, p. 206
3•7	Explain how 6 + 8 helped you solve 80 + 60.	*TLG*, p. 222
3•8	Explain how you found how many children ate scoops of ice cream.	*TLG*, p. 228

Portfolio Opportunities

Portfolios are a versatile tool for assessment. They help children reflect on their mathematical growth and help teachers understand and document that growth. Each unit identifies several student products that can be selected and stored in a portfolio. Here are some of the Unit 3 suggestions:

Lesson	Portfolio Opportunities	Where to Find It
3•3	Children explain how they found the answers to extended fact problems.	*TLG*, p. 200
3•4	Children explain how they found the difference in the number of points scored.	*TLG*, p. 206
3•7	Children explain how 6 + 8 helped them solve 80 + 60.	*TLG*, p. 222
3•8	Children explain how they found how many children ate scoops of ice cream.	*TLG*, p. 228

Periodic Assessment

Every Progress Check lesson includes opportunities to observe children's progress and to collect student products in a variety of ways—Self Assessment, Oral and Slate Assessment, Written Assessment, and an Open Response task. For more details, see the first page of Progress Check 3, Lesson 3-9 on page 230, of the *Teacher's Lesson Guide*.

Progress Check Modifications

Written Assessments are one way children demonstrate what they know. The table below shows modifications for the Written Assessment in this unit. Use these to maximize opportunities for children to demonstrate what they know. Modifications can be given individually or written on the board for the class.

Problem(s)	Modifications for Written Assessment
1, 9	For Problems 1 and 9, use your tool-kit coins to help you solve the problems.
3, 10	For Problems 3 and 10, skip count on your calculator to help you complete the counts.
8	For Problem 8, use your number grid to help you solve the problem.
11	For Problem 11, use the information in the graph to write two more things you know.

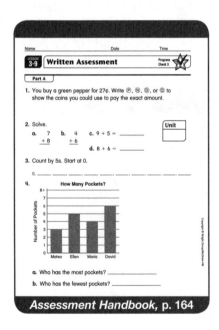

Assessment Handbook, p. 164

The Written Assessment for the Unit 3 Progress Check is on pages 164–166.

Open Response, *Buying from a Vending Machine*

Description

For this task, children show all possible coin combinations for a given amount.

Focus

- ◆ **Calculate the value of coin combinations.**
  [Operations and Computation Goal 2]
- ◆ **Make exchanges between coins.**
  [Measurement and Reference Frames Goal 4]

Implementation Tips

- ◆ Have children take out the tool-kit coins that represent the set Carlos has.
- ◆ Record coin symbols and values on the board.
- ◆ Review equivalencies for quarters, nickels, and dimes.

Modifications for Meeting Diverse Needs

- ◆ Provide calculators so children can skip-count to find the total value of the coins.
- ◆ Ask children to explain how they could change the problem to increase the number of coin combinations.

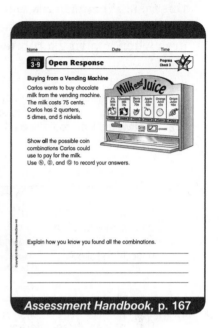

Assessment Handbook, p. 167

Improving Open Response Skills

After children complete the task, have them share their strategies for finding all the combinations. List some of the key features of their strategies—for example, starting with dimes. After the discussion, have children try to improve their work either by finding missing combinations or by organizing their combinations.

Note: The wording and formatting of the text on the student samples that follow may vary slightly from the actual task your children will complete. These minor discrepancies will not affect the implementation of the task.

Rubric

This rubric is designed to help you assess levels of mathematical performance on this task. It emphasizes mathematical understanding with only a mention of clarity of explanation. Consider the expectations of standardized tests in your area when applying a rubric. Modify this sample rubric as appropriate.

4   Lists seven different coin combinations that total 75¢. (One or more may be repeated.) Uses only coins specified in the problem. Attempts to explain a strategy that would lead to finding all possible combinations, but the explanation might be incomplete.

3   Lists at least five different coin combinations and most total 75¢. (One or more may be repeated.) Uses only coins specified in the problem. Attempts to explain a strategy. The explanation makes sense in the context of the problem, but it might be difficult to follow.

2   Lists at least three different coin combinations, and some might total 75¢. (One or more may be repeated.) Might use coins specified in the problem. Attempts to explain a strategy, but the explanation might apply to finding the total of a coin combination rather than finding different combinations of coins.

1   Attempts to list a few coin combinations, but most or all do not total 75¢. (One or more may be repeated.) Might use coins specified in the problem. Might attempt to explain a strategy, but the explanation does not provide evidence of a strategy for finding totals or finding different combinations.

0   Does not attempt to understand or to solve the problem.

Sample Student Responses

This Level 4 paper illustrates the following features: All seven coin combinations for 75¢ are listed. In the listed combinations, there is a pattern—first using two quarters, then no quarters, and finally one quarter. There is also a pattern in exchanging coins from one combination to the next. The explanation in words is incomplete.

This Level 4 paper illustrates the following features: All seven coin combinations for 75¢ with one repeated are listed. The combinations are organized so no quarters are on the left, one quarter is in the middle, and two quarters are on the right. The explanation begins to describe a strategy that would lead to finding all possible combinations, but the explanation is incomplete.

This Level 2 paper illustrates the following features: Three different coin combinations for 75¢ including one that does not total 75¢ are listed. An extra nickel is used in one combination. The explanation describes a strategy for finding a total for coin combinations, not for finding different combinations.

Name _____ Date _____ Time _____

LESSON 3·9

Open Response

Progress Check 3

Buying from a Vending Machine

Carlos wants to buy chocolate milk from the vending machine. The milk costs 75 cents and Carlos has 2 quarters, 5 dimes and 5 nickels.

Show **all** the possible coin combinations Carlos could use to pay for the milk. Use Ⓝ, Ⓓ, and Ⓠ to record your answers.

Explain how you know you found all the combinations.

I Add the Ⓠs and Ⓝsand Ⓠs.

This Level 3 paper illustrates the following features: Six different coin combinations for 75¢ are listed. (The combination of five dimes and five nickels is repeated, and the combination of one quarter, three dimes, and four nickels is repeated. One combination does not total 75¢.) There does not appear to be an organized strategy for listing the combinations. There is an attempt at explaining a strategy, but it is incomplete.

Name _____ Date _____ Time _____

LESSON 3·9

Open Response

Progress Check 3

Buying from a Vending Machine

Carlos wants to buy chocolate milk from the vending machine. The milk costs 75 cents and Carlos has 2 quarters, 5 dimes and 5 nickels.

Show **all** the possible coin combinations Carlos could use to pay for the milk. Use Ⓝ, Ⓓ, and Ⓠ to record your answers.

Explain how you know you found all the combinations.

How I found all the combination is that I add the 5Ⓝ and 5Ⓓ and Ⓠ Ⓝ what I got was a 75¢. (I just add to make sure the I got 75¢.)

so. 2 Ⓓ Ⓠ Ⓝ

Use with Lesson 3-09

2UO3L09M05

74 *Assessment Handbook*

This Level 1 paper illustrates the following features: One coin combination for 75¢ and four that do not total 75¢ are listed. Extra dimes are used in one of the combinations. The explanation starts to describe a strategy that could yield different combinations, but it does not relate directly to the other work on the page, and it is incomplete.

This Level 1 paper illustrates the following features: Two different coin combinations for 75¢ and two that do not total 75¢ are listed. The explanation provides no evidence of a strategy for finding totals or for finding different combinations.

Assessment Overview

In this unit, children further develop addition and subtraction strategies for solving number stories and doing mental arithmetic. Use the information in this section to develop your assessment plan for Unit 4.

Ongoing Assessment

Opportunities for using and collecting ongoing assessment information are highlighted in Informing Instruction and Recognizing Student Achievement notes. Student products, along with observations and suggested writing prompts, provide a range of useful assessment information.

Informing Instruction

The Informing Instruction notes highlight children's thinking and point out common misconceptions. Informing Instruction in Unit 4: Lessons 4-1, 4-2, 4-3, 4-5, and 4-6.

Recognizing Student Achievement

The Recognizing Student Achievement notes highlight specific tasks from which teachers can collect assessment data to monitor and document children's progress toward meeting Grade-Level Goals.

Lesson	Content Assessed	Where to Find It
4•1	**Solve number stories.** [Operations and Computation Goal 4]	*TLG*, p. 251
4•2	**Solve parts-and-total situations.** [Operations and Computation Goal 4]	*TLG*, p. 256
4•3	**Write equivalent names for $1.00.** [Number and Numeration Goal 5]	*TLG*, p. 263
4•4	**Read, show temperatures, and solve temperature-change problems.** [Measurement and Reference Frames Goal 5]	*TLG*, p. 269
4•5	**Estimate the total cost of two items.** [Operations and Computation Goal 3]	*TLG*, p. 275
4•6	**Tell time to the nearest quarter hour.** [Measurement and Reference Frames Goal 6]	*TLG*, p. 281
4•7	**Record addition facts.** [Operations and Computation Goal 1]	*TLG*, p. 286
4•8	**Make ballpark estimates.** [Operations and Computation Goal 3]	*TLG*, p. 291
4•9	**Solve problems involving addition of multidigit multiples of ten.** [Operations and Computation Goal 2]	*TLG*, p. 295

Math Boxes

Math Boxes, one of several types of tasks highlighted in the Recognizing Student Achievement notes, have an additional useful feature. Math Boxes in most lessons are paired or linked with Math Boxes in one or two other lessons that have similar problems. Paired or linked Math Boxes in Unit 4: 4-1 and 4-3; 4-2 and 4-4; 4-5, 4-7, and 4-9; and 4-6 and 4-8.

Writing/Reasoning Prompts

In Unit 4, a variety of writing prompts encourage children to explain their strategies and thinking, to reflect on their learning, and to make connections to other mathematics or life experiences. Here are some of the Unit 4 suggestions:

Lesson	Writing/Reasoning Prompts	Where to Find It
4◆3	Explain counting by 100s for 5 more spaces and describe a pattern.	*TLG*, p. 264
4◆4	Explain how you know how much change LaVon will receive.	*TLG*, p. 270
4◆7	Explain how you know a number is odd or even.	*TLG*, p. 286
4◆8	Explain why your answer to the change of temperature problem is correct.	*TLG*, p. 292
4◆9	Explain what time it will be in 12 hours.	*TLG*, p. 298

Portfolio Opportunities

Portfolios are a versatile tool for assessment. They help children reflect on their mathematical growth and help teachers understand and document that growth. Each unit identifies several student products that can be selected and stored in a portfolio. Here are some of the Unit 4 suggestions:

Lesson	Portfolio Opportunities	Where to Find It
4◆3	Children count by 100s for 5 more spaces and explain the number pattern.	*TLG*, p. 264
4◆4	Children explain how much change LaVon will receive.	*TLG*, p. 270
4◆7	Children explain how they know a number is odd or even.	*TLG*, p. 286
4◆8	Children explain how they know their answer to the change of temperature problem is correct.	*TLG*, p. 292
4◆9	Children explain what time it will be in 12 hours and how they solved the problem.	*TLG*, p. 298

Periodic Assessment

Every Progress Check lesson includes opportunities to observe children's progress and to collect student products in a variety of ways—Self Assessment, Oral and Slate Assessment, Written Assessment, and an Open Response task. For more details, see the first page of Progress Check 4, Lesson 4-10 on page 300, of the *Teacher's Lesson Guide*.

Progress Check Modifications

Written Assessments are one way children demonstrate what they know. The table below shows modifications for the Written Assessment in this unit. Use these to maximize opportunities for children to demonstrate what they know. Modifications can be given individually or written on the board for the class.

Problem(s)	Modifications for Written Assessment
3	For Problem 3, build each number on a place-value mat using base-10 blocks.
4	For Problem 4, explain how you can tell whether a number is even or odd.
6	For Problem 6, use tool-kit coins to help you solve the problem.
8	For Problem 8, use your number grid to help you solve the problems.

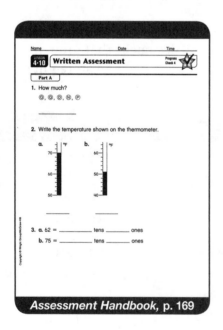

Assessment Handbook, p. 169

The Written Assessment for the Unit 4 Progress Check is on pages 169–171.

Open Response, *Finding the Largest Sum*

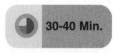

Description

For this task, children create and add two 2-digit numbers to find the largest possible sum.

Focus

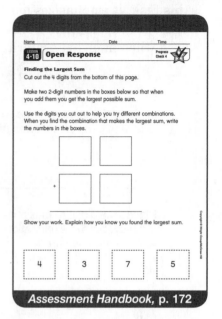

Assessment Handbook, p. 172

◆ **Identify the values of the digits in the 2-digit numbers.**
[Number and Numeration Goal 2]

◆ **Compare and order whole numbers.**
[Number and Numeration Goal 7]

◆ **Solves problems involving the addition of 2-digit whole numbers.**
[Operations and Computation Goal 2]

Implementation Tips

◆ Provide base-10 blocks and place-value mats.

Modifications for Meeting Diverse Needs

◆ Have children build their numbers with base-10 blocks and record their total. Have them compare their totals before answering the problem.

◆ Have children find the largest possible difference using four different digits. Have them compare the strategies for finding the largest sum and the largest difference. Which features of the strategies are alike and which ones are different?

Improving Open Response Skills

Before children complete the task, have them look over the problem and generate a list of vocabulary words that they might use in the explanation—for example, *digits, tens place, ones place, sum, greater than, less than,* and *compare*.

Note: The wording and formatting of the text on the student samples that follow may vary slightly from the actual task your children will complete. These minor discrepancies will not affect the implementation of the task.

Rubric

This rubric is designed to help you assess levels of mathematical performance on this task. It emphasizes mathematical understanding with only a mention of clarity of explanation. Consider the expectations of standardized tests in your area when applying a rubric. Modify this sample rubric as appropriate.

4	Places the digits to maximize the sum. Finds the sum. Clearly and completely explains the strategy used. Uses mathematical vocabulary such as *greater than, less than, tens place, ones place,* and *sum.*
3	Places the digits to maximize the sum. Finds the sum. Attempts to explain the strategy, but the explanation might not be complete. Might not use mathematical vocabulary.
2	Might place digits to make the largest possible sum. Finds the correct sum for the numbers written. Might attempt to explain a strategy, but there is no evidence of having a strategy that would lead to solving the problem.
1	Places digits without any evidence of a strategy. Might make computation errors. The explanation is missing or makes no sense in the context of the problem.
0	Does not attempt to understand or solve the problem.

Sample Student Responses

This Level 4 paper illustrates the following features: The digits are placed to maximize the sum. The sum is correct. Incorporating mathematical language, the explanation clearly describes how place value was used to determine the addends.

This Level 4 paper illustrates the following features: The digits are placed to maximize the sum. The sum is correct. Incorporating mathematical language, the explanation clearly describes how a guess-and-check strategy was used to determine the addends.

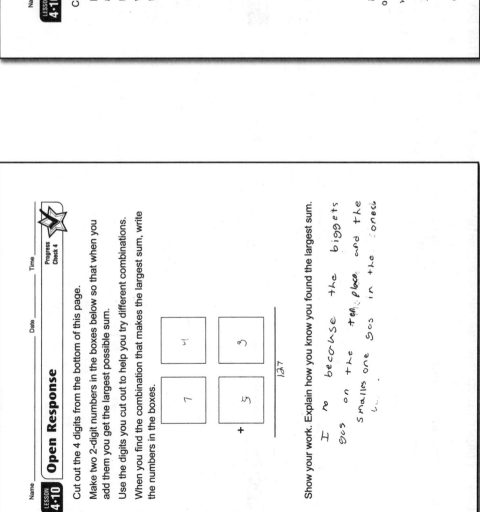

Name _____ Date _____ Time _____

Progress Check 4

LESSON 4·10 **Open Response**

Cut out the 4 digits from the bottom of this page.

Make two 2-digit numbers in the boxes below so that when you add them you get the largest possible sum.

Use the digits you cut out to help you try different combinations.

When you find the combination that makes the largest sum, write the numbers in the boxes.

Show your work. Explain how you know you found the largest sum.

I no because the biggets 8os on the ten place and the smalles one 5os in the ones

Name _____ Date _____ Time _____

Progress Check 4

LESSON 4·10 **Open Response**

Cut out the 4 digits from the bottom of this page.

Make two 2-digit numbers in the boxes below so that when you add them you get the largest possible sum.

Use the digits you cut out to help you try different combinations.

When you find the combination that makes the largest sum, write the numbers in the boxes.

Show your work. Explain how you know you found the largest sum.

All the some to added looked at all the other ones that was the highest some. I think that is the largest some becaus I tried

This Level 3 paper illustrates the following features: The digits are placed to maximize the sum. The sum is correct. The explanation provides evidence that there is an understanding of how a guess-and-check strategy could be used to solve the problem, but the explanation is incomplete.

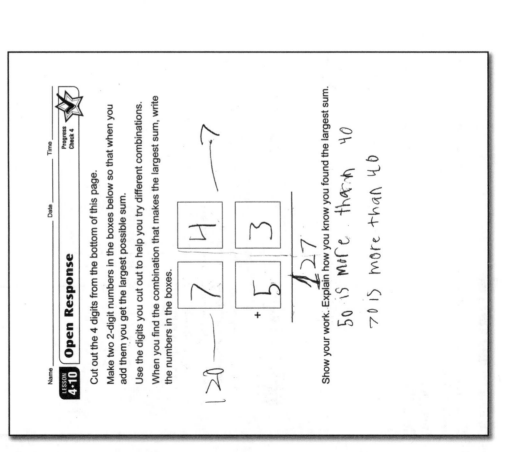

This Level 3 paper illustrates the following features: The digits are placed to maximize the sum. The sum is correct. The explanation provides evidence that there is an understanding of how to build and compare numbers to solve the problem, but the explanation is incomplete.

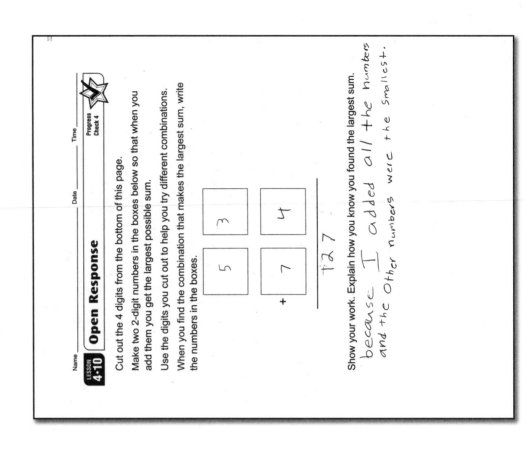

This Level 1 paper illustrates the following features: The recorded addends do not maximize the sum. The sum is correct for the recorded addends. The explanation is missing.

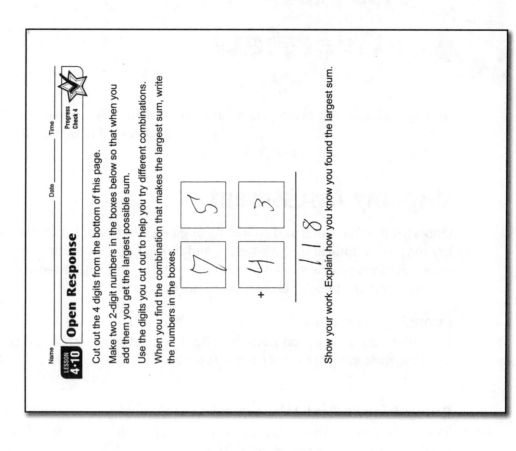

Name _____ Date _____ Time _____

LESSON
4·10
Open Response

Progress Check 4

Cut out the 4 digits from the bottom of this page.

Make two 2-digit numbers in the boxes below so that when you add them you get the largest possible sum.

Use the digits you cut out to help you try different combinations.

When you find the combination that makes the largest sum, write the numbers in the boxes.

7 5

+ 4 3

118

Show your work. Explain how you know you found the largest sum.

This Level 2 paper illustrates the following features: The sum is correct for the recorded addends. The explanation describes a strategy that would not lead to a correct solution, but indicates some understanding that the size of the digits matters.

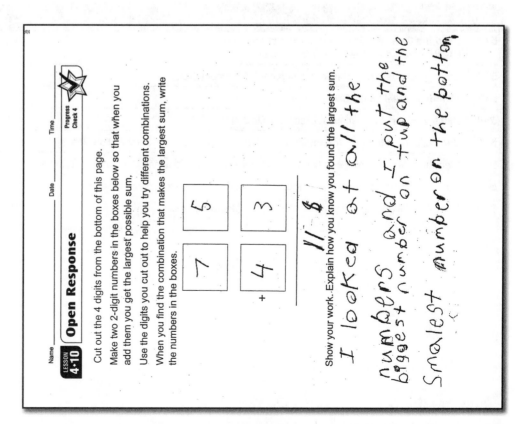

Name _____ Date _____ Time _____

LESSON
4·10
Open Response

Progress Check 4

Cut out the 4 digits from the bottom of this page.

Make two 2-digit numbers in the boxes below so that when you add them you get the largest possible sum.

Use the digits you cut out to help you try different combinations.

When you find the combination that makes the largest sum, write the numbers in the boxes.

7 5

+ 4 3

11-8

Show your work. Explain how you know you found the largest sum.

I looked at all the numbers and I put the biggest number on twp and the smallest number on the bottom.

Assessment Overview

In this unit, children explore, compare, and contrast the properties of 2- and 3-dimensional figures. Use the information in this section to develop your assessment plan for Unit 5.

Ongoing Assessment

Opportunities for using and collecting ongoing assessment information are highlighted in Informing Instruction and Recognizing Student Achievement notes. Student products, along with observations and suggested writing prompts, provide a range of useful assessment information.

Informing Instruction
The Informing Instruction notes highlight children's thinking and point out common misconceptions. Informing Instruction in Unit 5: Lessons 5-3, 5-5, and 5-6.

Recognizing Student Achievement
The Recognizing Student Achievement notes highlight specific tasks from which teachers can collect assessment data to monitor and document children's progress toward meeting Grade-Level Goals.

Lesson	Content Assessed	Where to Find It
5◆1	**Read the time and match it to its digital notation.** [Measurement and Reference Frames Goal 6]	*TLG*, p. 319
5◆2	**Use a straightedge to draw a line segment.** [Geometry Goal 1]	*TLG*, p. 324
5◆3	**Identify parallel lines.** [Geometry Goal 1]	*TLG*, p. 329
5◆4	**Name 2-dimensional shapes.** [Geometry Goal 2]	*TLG*, p. 333
5◆5	**Use ballpark estimation for addition problems.** [Operations and Computation Goal 3]	*TLG*, p. 339
5◆6	**Find the difference between two 2-digit numbers.** [Operations and Computation Goal 2]	*TLG*, p. 347
5◆7	**Complete patterns in a number grid.** [Patterns, Functions, and Algebra Goal 1]	*TLG*, p. 353
5◆8	**Complete 2-dimensional symmetric shapes.** [Geometry Goal 3]	*TLG*, p. 357

Math Boxes

Math Boxes, one of several types of tasks highlighted in the Recognizing Student Achievement notes, have an additional useful feature. Math Boxes in most lessons are paired or linked with Math Boxes in one or two other lessons that have similar problems. Paired or linked Math Boxes in Unit 5: 5-1 and 5-3; 5-2 and 5-4; 5-5 and 5-7; and 5-6 and 5-8.

Writing/Reasoning Prompts

In Unit 5, a variety of writing prompts encourage children to explain their strategies and thinking, to reflect on their learning, and to make connections to other mathematics or life experiences. Here are some of the Unit 5 suggestions:

Lesson	Writing/Reasoning Prompts	Where to Find It
5♦3	Explain how you know you made the largest number.	TLG, p. 330
5♦4	Explain how you know your numbers are even.	TLG, p. 336
5♦5	Explain the strategy you used to fill in the number grid.	TLG, p. 341
5♦6	Explain how you found how many children traveled to school.	TLG, p. 347

Portfolio Opportunities

Portfolios are a versatile tool for assessment. They help children reflect on their mathematical growth and help teachers understand and document that growth. Each unit identifies several student products that can be selected and stored in a portfolio. Here are some of the Unit 5 suggestions:

Lesson	Portfolio Opportunities	Where to Find It
5♦1	Children record how they divide eggs among nests.	TLG, p. 318
5♦4	Children name 2-dimensional shapes.	TLG, p. 333
5♦4	Children make arrays with centimeter cubes and record the number of rows, how many in each row, and how many in all.	TLG, p. 335
5♦5	Children use ballpark estimation for addition problems.	TLG, p. 339
5♦6	Children explain how they found how many children traveled to school in all.	TLG, p. 347

Periodic Assessment

Every Progress Check lesson includes opportunities to observe children's progress and to collect student products in a variety of ways—Self Assessment, Oral and Slate Assessment, Written Assessment, and an Open Response task. For more details, see the first page of Progress Check 5, Lesson 5-9 on page 360, of the *Teacher's Lesson Guide*.

Progress Check Modifications

Written Assessments are one way children demonstrate what they know. The table below shows modifications for the Written Assessment in this unit. Use these to maximize opportunities for children to demonstrate what they know. Modifications can be given individually or written on the board for the class.

Problem(s)	Modifications for Written Assessment
2	For Problem 2, use a calculator to help you complete the count.
3	For Problem 3, build each number on a place-value mat using base-10 blocks. Compare the numbers you have built.
12	For Problem 12, explain how you know that line segment *EF* is not parallel to line segment *AB*.
13	For Problem 13, cut out the shapes and fold them to find the lines of symmetry. *Note to the teacher—provide an enlarged copy of these shapes for children to cut out.*

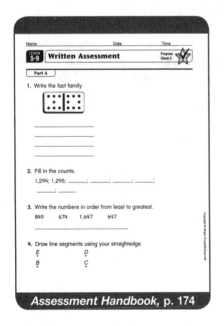

Assessment Handbook, p. 174

The Written Assessment for the Unit 5 Progress Check is on pages 174–176.

Open Response, *Making Polygons*

Description

For this task, children use four triangle pattern blocks to make polygons and figures that are not polygons and to describe why some figures are not polygons.

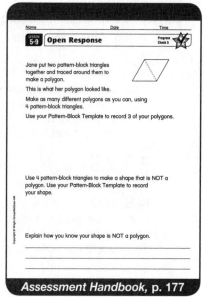

Assessment Handbook, p. 177

Focus

◆ **Identify, describe, and model plane figures.**
[Geometry Goal 2]

Implementation Tips

◆ Have children find shapes in the room that represent polygons.

◆ Remind children to use all four triangles to make their figures.

◆ Provide enough pattern blocks so children can keep the polygons they build to help them compare the figures. They might build their figures on quarter-sheets of paper to facilitate rotating them. Remind children that rotated figures are not different.

Modifications for Meeting Diverse Needs

◆ Have children identify and list objects in the room that could represent polygons and some that do not represent polygons (instead of building the shapes using pattern-block triangles).

◆ Have children record at least two figures that are not polygons—each one illustrating a different attribute that is missing. For example, a figure with a hole in the middle or a figure where the sides intersect and continue instead of meet.

Improving Open Response Skills

Before children begin the task, have them read through the task together and articulate a list of the necessary components of the task. Post this list during the task implementation. For example, every figure on the page has to be made from four pattern-block triangles; there should be three polygons made from the triangles; the explanation should match the drawing of the figure that is not a polygon; the explanation should say something that is true about polygons but not true about the figure that is not a polygon.

Note: The wording and formatting of the text on the student samples that follow may vary slightly from the actual task your children will complete. These minor discrepancies will not affect the implementation of the task.

Rubric

This rubric is designed to help you assess levels of mathematical performance on this task. It emphasizes mathematical understanding with only a mention of clarity of explanation. Consider the expectations of standardized tests in your area when applying a rubric. Modify this sample rubric as appropriate.

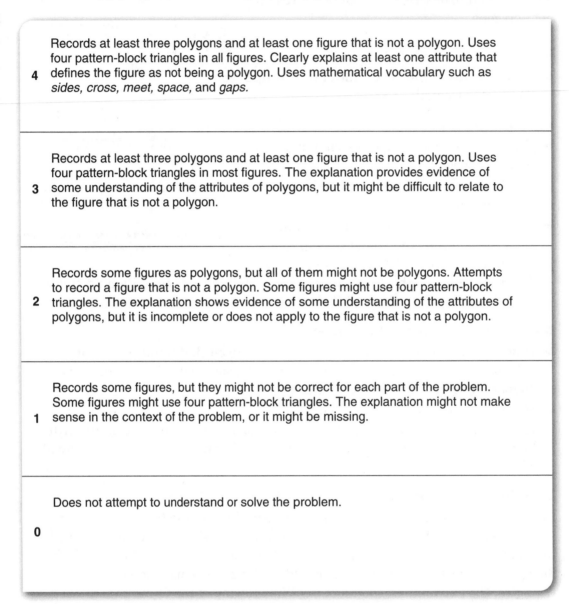

4 Records at least three polygons and at least one figure that is not a polygon. Uses four pattern-block triangles in all figures. Clearly explains at least one attribute that defines the figure as not being a polygon. Uses mathematical vocabulary such as *sides, cross, meet, space,* and *gaps.*

3 Records at least three polygons and at least one figure that is not a polygon. Uses four pattern-block triangles in most figures. The explanation provides evidence of some understanding of the attributes of polygons, but it might be difficult to relate to the figure that is not a polygon.

2 Records some figures as polygons, but all of them might not be polygons. Attempts to record a figure that is not a polygon. Some figures might use four pattern-block triangles. The explanation shows evidence of some understanding of the attributes of polygons, but it is incomplete or does not apply to the figure that is not a polygon.

1 Records some figures, but they might not be correct for each part of the problem. Some figures might use four pattern-block triangles. The explanation might not make sense in the context of the problem, or it might be missing.

0 Does not attempt to understand or solve the problem.

Sample Student Responses

This Level 4 paper illustrates the following features: Three polygons and one figure that is not a polygon are recorded. Four triangles are used in all figures. The explanation describes why the figure is not a polygon—it has space in the middle.

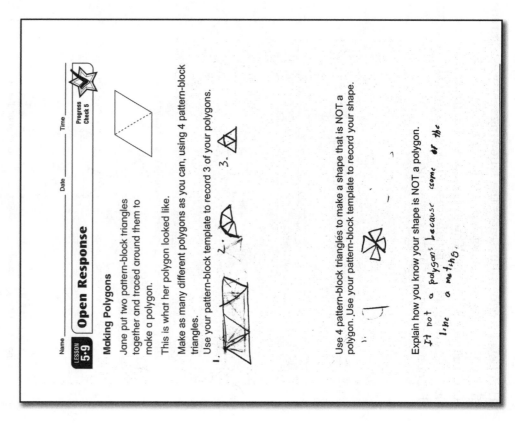

This Level 4 paper illustrates the following features: Three polygons and one figure that is not a polygon are recorded. Four triangles are used in all figures. The explanation describes why the figure is not a polygon—some of the lines meet (intersect).

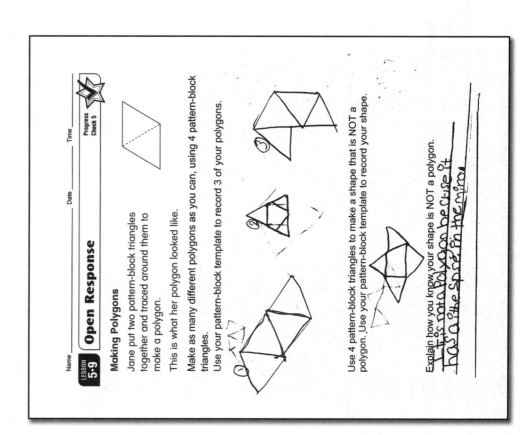

This Level 3 paper illustrates the following features: Three polygons and one figure that is not a polygon are recorded. Four triangles are used in all figures. The explanation demonstrates some understanding of the attributes of polygons, but it states that there are no straight lines in the figure, which is incorrect for the recorded figure.

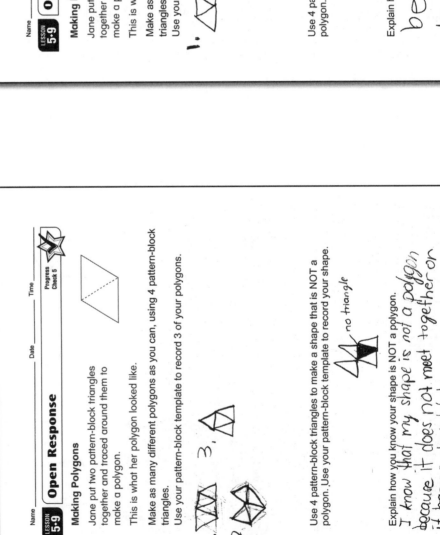

This Level 3 paper illustrates the following features: Three polygons and one figure that is not a polygon are recorded. Four triangles are used in all figures. The explanation demonstrates some understanding of the attributes of polygons, but the reasoning is difficult to relate to the recorded figure.

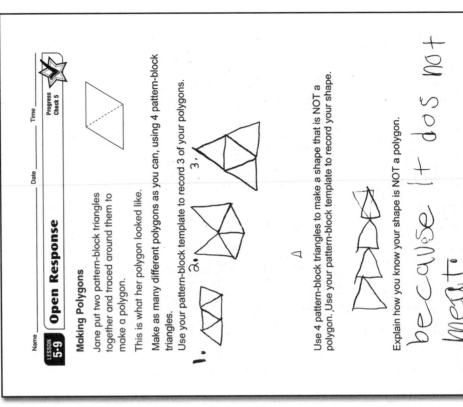

This Level 1 paper illustrates the following features: Four polygons and one figure that is not a polygon are recorded. The figure labeled 1 is not a polygon. Four triangles are used in some figures. There is no evidence of an understanding of the attributes of polygons.

This Level 2 paper illustrates the following features: Two polygons and two figures that are not polygons are recorded. Four triangles are used in all figures. The explanation indicates some understanding of the attributes of polygons—that they cannot be open—but it uses vague language and is difficult to relate to the recorded figure.

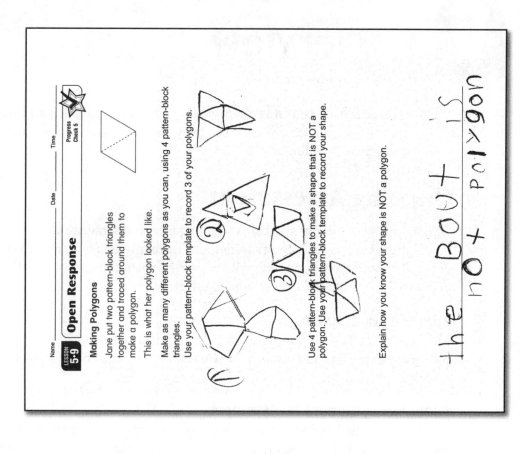

Name _____ Date _____ Time _____

LESSON 5·9 Open Response Progress Check 5

Making Polygons

Jane put two pattern-block triangles together and traced around them to make a polygon.

This is what her polygon looked like.

Make as many different polygons as you can, using 4 pattern-block triangles.
Use your pattern-block template to record 3 of your polygons.

Use 4 pattern-block triangles to make a shape that is NOT a polygon. Use your pattern-block template to record your shape.

Explain how you know your shape is NOT a polygon.

the Bout is not polygon

Name _____ Date _____ Time _____

LESSON 5·9 Open Response Progress Check 5

Making Polygons

Jane put two pattern-block triangles together and traced around them to make a polygon.

This is what her polygon looked like.

Make as many different polygons as you can, using 4 pattern-block triangles.
Use your pattern-block template to record 3 of your polygons.

Use 4 pattern-block triangles to make a shape that is NOT a polygon. Use your pattern-block template to record your shape.

Explain how you know your shape is NOT a polygon.

It has an open space on the top

Assessment Overview

In this unit, children continue their work with number stories and begin to explore a subtraction algorithm. Use the information in this section to develop your assessment plan for Unit 6.

Ongoing Assessment

Opportunities for using and collecting ongoing assessment information are highlighted in Informing Instruction and Recognizing Student Achievement notes. Student products, along with observations and suggested writing prompts, provide a range of useful assessment information.

Informing Instruction
The Informing Instruction notes highlight children's thinking and point out common misconceptions. Informing Instruction in Unit 6: Lessons 6-2, 6-3, 6-4, and 6-5.

Recognizing Student Achievement
The Recognizing Student Achievement notes highlight specific tasks from which teachers can collect assessment data to monitor and document children's progress toward meeting Grade-Level Goals.

Lesson	Content Assessed	Where to Find It
6•1	Add three and four numbers. [Operations and Computation Goal 2]	*TLG*, p. 381
6•2	Solve comparison number stories. [Operations and Computation Goal 4]	*TLG*, p. 387
6•3	Read graphs. [Data and Chance Goal 2]	*TLG*, p. 394
6•4	Solve number stories. [Operations and Computation Goal 2]	*TLG*, p. 398
6•5	Use probability language. [Data and Chance Goal 3]	*TLG*, p. 405
6•6	Create $1.00 using different coin combinations. [Measurement and Reference Frames Goal 4]	*TLG*, p. 409
6•7	Combine equal groups to find the total. [Operations and Computation Goal 4]	*TLG*, p. 413
6•8	Draw rectangular arrays. [Operations and Computation Goal 4]	*TLG*, p. 422
6•9	Draw and measure a 3-inch line segment. [Measurement and Reference Frames Goal 1]	*TLG*, p. 427
6•10	Use counters and drawings to solve equal-sharing problems. [Operations and Computation Goal 4]	*TLG*, p. 432

Math Boxes

Math Boxes, one of several types of tasks highlighted in the Recognizing Student Achievement notes, have an additional useful feature. Math Boxes in most lessons are paired or linked with Math Boxes in one or two other lessons that have similar problems. Paired or linked Math Boxes in Unit 6: 6-1, 6-3, and 6-5; 6-2 and 6-4; 6-6, 6-8, and 6-10; 6-7 and 6-9.

Writing/Reasoning Prompts

In Unit 6, a variety of writing prompts encourage children to explain their strategies and thinking, to reflect on their learning, and to make connections to other mathematics or life experiences. Here are some of the Unit 6 suggestions:

Lesson	Writing/Reasoning Prompts	Where to Find It
6•2	Explain how you know you have written all the possible coin combinations for 30 cents.	*TLG*, p. 388
6•3	Explain how many more inches you would need to add to the line segment to make it 10 inches.	*TLG*, p. 394
6•6	Draw a shape that has a line of symmetry, and then draw another shape that has more than one line of symmetry.	*TLG*, p. 410
6•7	Explain whether Lauren is older or younger than you and what strategy you used.	*TLG*, p. 416

Portfolio Opportunities

Portfolios are a versatile tool for assessment. They help children reflect on their mathematical growth and help teachers understand and document that growth. Each unit identifies several student products that can be selected and stored in a portfolio. Here are some of the Unit 6 suggestions:

Lesson	Portfolio Opportunities	Where to Find It
6•2	Children explain how they know they have written all the possible coin combinations for 30 cents.	*TLG*, p. 388
6•3	Children explain how many more inches they would need to add to the line segment to make it 10 inches.	*TLG*, p. 394
6•6	Children determine and record coin combinations using Ⓝ, Ⓓ, and Ⓠ.	*TLG*, p. 409
6•7	Children explain whether Lauren is older or younger than they are and what strategy they used.	*TLG*, p. 416
6•10	Children show their work for solving an equal-sharing problem: *14 candies shared by 2 people.*	*TLG*, p. 432

Periodic Assessment

Every Progress Check lesson includes opportunities to observe children's progress and to collect student products in a variety of ways—Self Assessment, Oral and Slate Assessment, Written Assessment, and an Open Response task. For more details, see the first page of Progress Check 6, Lesson 6-11 on page 434, of the *Teacher's Lesson Guide*.

Progress Check Modifications

Written Assessments are one way children demonstrate what they know. The table below shows modifications for the Written Assessment in this unit. Use these to maximize opportunities for children to demonstrate what they know. Modifications can be given individually or written on the board for the class.

Problem(s)	Modifications for Written Assessment
4	For Problem 4, build each number on a place-value mat using base-10 blocks. Compare the numbers you have built.
5, 8, 9, 10	For Problems 5, 8, 9, and 10, use your number grid to help you solve the problems.
6	For Problem 6, record an addition and a multiplication number model. Explain how both number models fit the problem.
7	For Problem 7, draw and label pictures to model the problem.

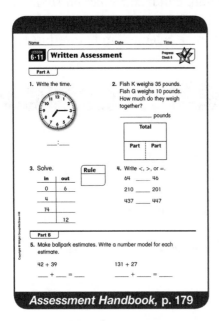

Assessment Handbook, p. 179

The Written Assessment for the Unit 6 Progress Check is on pages 179–180.

Open Response, *Counting Cookies*

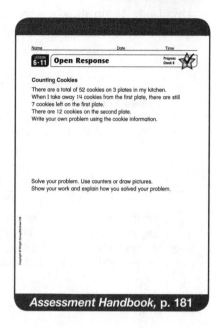

Description

For this task, children write and solve an addition or subtraction number story using given information.

Focus

◆ **Solve problems involving the addition and subtraction of 2-digit whole numbers.**
[Operations and Computation Goal 2]

◆ **Write and solve number sentences involving addition and subtraction.**
[Patterns, Functions, and Algebra Goal 2]

Implementation Tips

◆ Read the information from the problem together and list what is known on the board.

◆ Have number grids available for doing the computation.

Assessment Handbook, p. 181

Modifications for Meeting Diverse Needs

◆ Use sheets of paper to represent the plates and encourage children to use counters to model the information they have.

◆ Have children write and solve a multistep problem.

Improving Open Response Skills

After children complete the task, have them reflect on what was difficult and what was easy about the task, and describe how they think they could improve their work. Have children work in groups to write, solve, and explain a new problem based on the information given in the Open Response task.

Note: The wording and formatting of the text on the student samples that follow may vary slightly from the actual task your children will complete. These minor discrepancies will not affect the implementation of the task.

Rubric

This rubric is designed to help you assess levels of mathematical performance on this task. It emphasizes mathematical understanding with only a mention of clarity of explanation. Consider the expectations of standardized tests in your area when applying a rubric. Modify this sample rubric as appropriate.

4	Writes a problem that requires only the given information for a solution and makes sense based on the given information. Solves the problem and computes correctly. Clearly explains the solution strategy.
3	Writes a problem that requires only the given information for a solution and makes sense based on the given information. Solves the problem with only minor computation errors. The explanation might be incomplete, but it demonstrates an understanding of the problem.
2	Writes a problem related to the given information, but it might be incomplete or rely on new information. Attempts to solve the problem but might not have found the solution. The explanation might be confusing, or it might not describe the strategy used.
1	Attempts to write a problem related to the given information. Attempts to solve the problem but there might be errors in the strategy or in the computation. The explanation might not make sense in the context of the problem, or it might be missing.
0	Does not attempt to understand or solve the problem.

Sample Student Responses

This Level 4 paper illustrates the following features: The problem is written using only the information provided. The problem is solved, and the computation is correct. The explanation describes the solution steps in words.

This Level 4 paper illustrates the following features: The problem is written using only the information provided. The problem is solved, and the computation is correct. The explanation illustrates the solution steps with pictures and a number model.

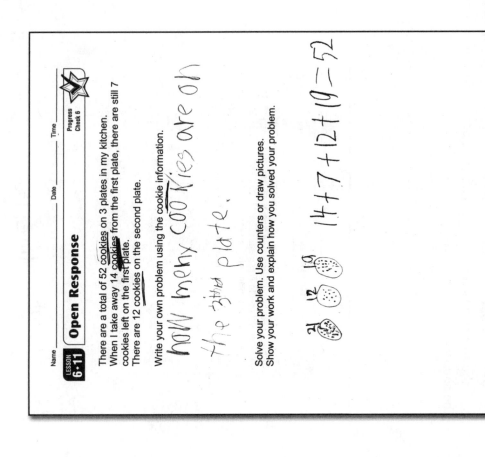

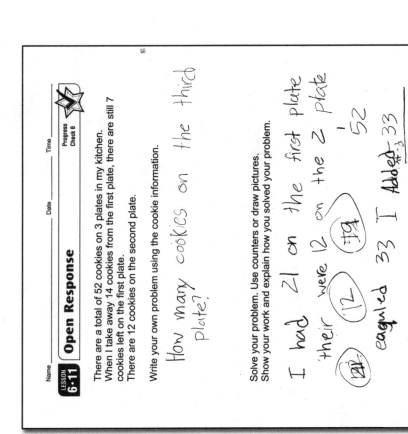

This Level 3 paper illustrates the following features: The problem is written using only the information provided. The problem is solved, and the computation is correct. The explanation illustrates some of the solution steps with pictures and a number model.

Open Response

There are a total of 52 cookies on 3 plates in my kitchen.
When I take away 14 cookies from the first plate, there are still 7 cookies left on the first plate.
There are 12 cookies on the second plate.

Write your own problem using the cookie information.

How many cookies left?

Solve your problem. Use counters or draw pictures.
Show your work and explain how you solved your problem.

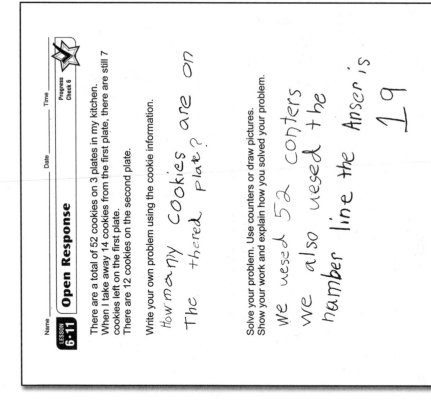

+21
12
33

There are 19 cookies on the 3 plate.

This Level 3 paper illustrates the following features: The problem is written using only the information provided. The problem is solved, and the computation is correct. The explanation describes some of the solution steps in words.

Open Response

There are a total of 52 cookies on 3 plates in my kitchen.
When I take away 14 cookies from the first plate, there are still 7 cookies left on the first plate.
There are 12 cookies on the second plate.

Write your own problem using the cookie information.

How many cookies are on the thered plate?

Solve your problem. Use counters or draw pictures.
Show your work and explain how you solved your problem.

We vesed 52 conters
we also vesed the
number line the Anser is
19

This Level 2 paper illustrates the following features: The problem is written using some provided and some additional information, and the problem makes sense. The problem is solved, and there is an attempt to illustrate some of the solution steps.

Name _____ Date _____ Time _____

LESSON
6·11
Open Response

Progress
Check 6

There are a total of 52 cookies on 3 plates in my kitchen.
When I take away 14 cookies from the first plate, there are still 7
cookies left on the first plate.
There are 12 cookies on the second plate.

Write your own problem using the cookie information.
I had 14 cookies. My mom took away 12 cookies. How many do I have now? 2 cookies

14
-12
02

Solve your problem. Use counters or draw pictures.
Show your work and explain how you solved your problem.

This Level 1 paper illustrates the following features: The problem is written using some provided and some additional information, but some information is missing. The problem is incomplete. There is a solution. There is an attempt to illustrate some of the solution steps, but the pictures do not relate to the problem. The number sentence includes information that was not in the problem.

Name _____ Date _____ Time _____

LESSON
6·11
Open Response

Progress
Check 6

There are a total of 52 cookies on 3 plates in my kitchen.
When I take away 14 cookies from the first plate, there are still 7
cookies left on the first plate.
There are 12 cookies on the second plate.

Write your own problem using the cookie information.
I ate 17 cookie. How many cookie are left? 21-17=4

Solve your problem. Use counters or draw pictures.
Show your work and explain how you solved your problem.

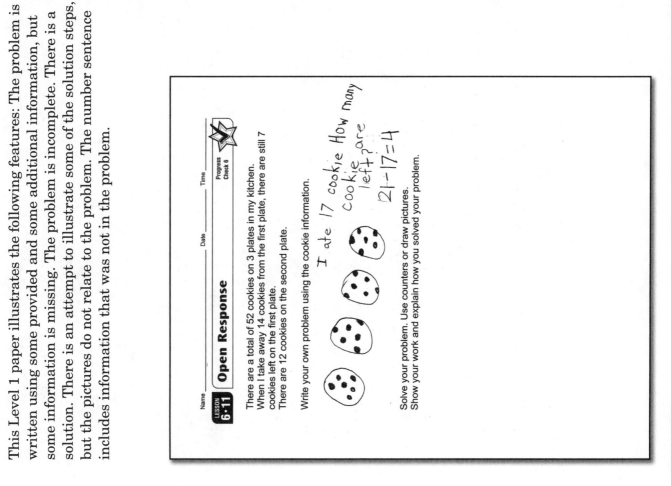

Mid-Year Assessment Goals

The Mid-Year Assessment (pages 223–226) provides an additional opportunity that you may use as part of your balanced assessment plan. It covers some of the important concepts and skills presented in *Second Grade Everyday Mathematics*. It should be used to complement the ongoing and periodic assessments that appear within lessons and at the end of units. The following table provides the goals for all the problems in the Mid-Year Assessment.

Problem(s)	Grade-Level Goal
1, 2	**Measurement and Reference Frames 5:** Read temperature on both the Fahrenheit and Celsius scales.
3, 4, 5, 6	**Number and Numeration 4:** Recognize numbers as odd or even.
7	**Measurement and Reference Frames 4:** Make exchanges between coins and bills.
8, 9	**Measurement and Reference Frames 5:** Read temperature on both the Fahrenheit and Celsius scales.
10	**Measurement and Reference Frames 4:** Make exchanges between coins and bills.
11	**Number and Numeration 4:** Recognize numbers as odd or even.
12, 13	**Measurement and Reference Frames 4:** Make exchanges between coins and bills.
14	**Measurement and Reference Frames 3:** Describe relationships between days in a week and hours in a day.
15	**Measurement and Reference Frames 4:** Make exchanges between coins and bills.
16, 17	**Measurement and Reference Frames 3:** Describe relationships between days in a week and hours in a day.

Assessment Overview

In this unit, children continue their work with number patterns, computation, and data analysis. Use the information in this section to develop your assessment plan for Unit 7.

Ongoing Assessment

Opportunities for using and collecting ongoing assessment information are highlighted in Informing Instruction and Recognizing Student Achievement notes. Student products, along with observations and suggested writing prompts, provide a range of useful assessment information.

Informing Instruction
The Informing Instruction notes highlight children's thinking and point out common misconceptions. Informing Instruction in Unit 7: Lessons 7-3, 7-4, 7-5, and 7-8.

Recognizing Student Achievement
The Recognizing Student Achievement notes highlight specific tasks from which teachers can collect assessment data to monitor and document children's progress toward meeting Grade-Level Goals.

Lesson	Content Assessed	Where to Find It
7♦1	**Count by 2s.** [Number and Numeration Goal 1]	*TLG*, p. 545
7♦2	**Find the difference between 2-digit numbers and any higher multiple of 10.** [Operations and Computation Goal 2]	*TLG*, p. 551
7♦3	**Solve addition problems with multiple addends.** [Operations and Computation Goal 2]	*TLG*, p. 557
7♦4	**Use a rule to follow a pattern.** [Patterns, Functions, and Algebra Goal 1]	*TLG*, p. 563
7♦5	**Draw a 5-by-3 array.** [Operations and Computation Goal 4]	*TLG*, p. 568
7♦6	**Compare standard and metric units of length.** [Measurement and Reference Frames Goal 1]	*TLG*, p. 571
7♦7	**Tell time to the quarter-hour.** [Measurement and Reference Frames Goal 6]	*TLG*, p. 580
7♦8	**Find the median.** [Data and Chance Goal 2]	*TLG*, p. 583

Math Boxes

Math Boxes, one of several types of tasks highlighted in the Recognizing Student Achievement notes, have an additional useful feature. Math Boxes in most lessons are paired or linked with Math Boxes in one or two other lessons that have similar problems. Paired or linked Math Boxes in Unit 7: 7-1 and 7-3; 7-2 and 7-4; 7-5 and 7-7; and 7-6 and 7-8.

Writing/Reasoning Prompts

In Unit 7, a variety of writing prompts encourage children to explain their strategies and thinking, to reflect on their learning, and to make connections to other mathematics or life experiences. Here are some of the Unit 7 suggestions:

Lesson	Writing/Reasoning Prompts	Where to Find It
7◆1	Describe any patterns you see.	*TLG*, p. 547
7◆4	Explain how you figured out how many groups of 3 you can make with 29 counters.	*TLG*, p. 563
7◆7	Tell the time 2 hours from the time shown.	*TLG*, p. 580
7◆8	Explain how you used your ballpark estimate to check your answer.	*TLG*, p. 586

Portfolio Opportunities

Portfolios are a versatile tool for assessment. They help children reflect on their mathematical growth and help teachers understand and document that growth. Each unit identifies several student products that can be selected and stored in a portfolio. Here are some of the Unit 7 suggestions:

Lesson	Portfolio Opportunities	Where to Find It
7◆4	Children explain how they made groups of 3 with 29 counters.	*TLG*, p. 563
7◆8	Children explain how to use a ballpark estimate to check an answer.	*TLG*, p. 586

Periodic Assessment

Every Progress Check lesson includes opportunities to observe children's progress and to collect student products in a variety of ways—Self Assessment, Oral and Slate Assessment, Written Assessment, and an Open Response task. For more details, see the first page of Progress Check 7, Lesson 7-9, page 588, of the *Teacher's Lesson Guide*.

Progress Check Modifications

Written Assessments are one way children demonstrate what they know. The table below shows modifications for the Written Assessment in this unit. Use these to maximize opportunities for children to demonstrate what they know. Modifications can be given individually or written on the board for the class.

Problem(s)	Modifications for Written Assessment
1	For Problem 1, use counters to solve the problem.
5, 6	For Problems 5 and 6, compare prisms and pyramids. List 2 ways a prism and a pyramid are alike and 2 ways they are different.
7	For Problem 7, use a number grid to find the sums.
9, 10	For Problems 9 and 10, for each set of numbers, write the individual numbers on stick-on notes, and arrange the stick-on notes in order before finding the landmarks.

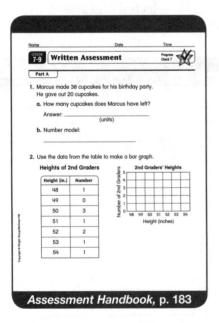

Assessment Handbook, p. 183

The Written Assessment for the Unit 7 Progress Check is on pages 183–185.

Open Response, *Dollars or Pennies?*

Description

For this task, children use patterns and rules to compare 2 ways of getting paid over time.

Focus

◆ **Use repeated addition to solve problems.**
   [Operations and Computation Goal 4]

◆ **Identify rules for patterns and use them to solve problems.**
   [Patterns, Functions, and Algebra Goal 1]

Implementation Tips

◆ Remind children to label their work.

◆ Remind children that $1.00 is equivalent to 100 pennies.

Modifications for Meeting Diverse Needs

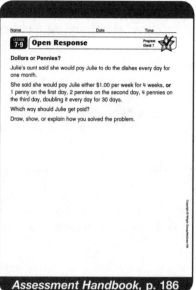

Name	Date	Time

7-9 Open Response   Progress Check 7

Dollars or Pennies?

Julie's aunt said she would pay Julie to do the dishes every day for one month.

She said she would pay Julie either $1.00 per week for 4 weeks, **or** 1 penny on the first day, 2 pennies on the second day, 4 pennies on the third day, doubling it every day for 30 days.

Which way should Julie get paid?

Draw, show, or explain how you solved the problem.

Assessment Handbook, p. 186

◆ Construct a table for children with the column headings *Day Number* and *Money Earned*. Have children complete the table. Remind them that they are looking at Julie's total earnings, not her earnings on a given day.

◆ Have children calculate how much Julie will earn in a month if she is paid using the doubling method (not just how much she will earn on the 30th day). *($10,737,418.23)* Have children use a calculator and emphasize organization.

Improving Open Response Skills

After children complete the task, display Level 4 of the rubric on the board or overhead and review it with the children. Have them translate Level 4 of the rubric into their words. Record the children's language on chart paper and display the description. Have children refer to the posted Level 4 description to improve their work before turning in their papers.

Note: The wording and formatting of the text on the student samples that follow may vary slightly from the actual task your children will complete. These minor discrepancies will not affect the implementation of the task.

Rubric

This rubric is designed to help you assess levels of mathematical performance on this task. It emphasizes mathematical understanding with only a mention of clarity of explanation. Consider the expectations of standardized tests in your area when applying a rubric. Modify this sample rubric as appropriate.

4   Concludes which method Julie should choose. Correctly explains how much Julie will earn with the $1.00-per-week method. Clearly justifies which method results in a greater total. Shows all steps of the computation used and all computation is correct through Day 10. There might be minor errors after Day 10.

3   Concludes which method Julie should choose. Justifies which method results in a greater total. There might be minor errors in the computation. Shows most of the steps used to solve the problem, but they might be difficult to follow.

2   Chooses the method that is justified by the work. There is some evidence of understanding how to double in the context of the problem, but there might be errors in the computation. Attempts to explain or show work, but the explanation or work might be confusing or unclear.

1   Attempts to solve the problem, but there might be errors in the computation and notation. The explanation might not make sense in the context of the problem or it might be incorrect.

0   Does not attempt to understand or solve the problem.

This Level 4 paper illustrates the following features: The work is labeled to show how the earnings accumulate daily and weekly according to the two payment methods. The computation is correct for both methods. The explanation states the answer and describes that it is possible to determine which method will result in more money.

This Level 4 paper illustrates the following features: The work is labeled to show how the earnings accumulate daily. The computation is correct. The explanation states the answer and describes that by the tenth day, the daily earnings surpass $4.00, which is the amount that would be earned during the entire month using the other method.

Name _____ Date _____ Time _____

LESSON 7·9

Open Response

Progress Check 7

Julie's aunt told her that she would pay her to do the dishes every day for one month.

She said she would pay Julie either $1.00 per week for 4 weeks or 1 penny on the first day, 2 pennies on the 2nd day, 4 pennies on the 3rd day, doubling it every day for 30 days.

Which way should Julie get paid? 2nd way

Draw, show, or explain how you solved the problem.

1¢
2¢
3¢
4 8¢
5 16¢
6 32¢
7 64¢
8 1.28
9 2.56
10 5.12
11 10.24

1.00
21.00
31.00
41.00
_____
4 dollers

I tride the fist way and she only had 4 Dollers. Then I tride the second way and she had 10.24 $9n only 11 Days.

If you try it the second you will have more then 4$.

Name _____ Date _____ Time _____

LESSON 7·9

Open Response

Progress Check 7

Julie's aunt told her that she would pay her to do the dishes every day for one month.

She said she would pay Julie either $1.00 per week for 4 weeks or 1 penny on the first day, 2 pennies on the 2nd day, 4 pennies on the 3rd day, doubling it every day for 30 days.

Which way should Julie get paid?

Draw, show, or explain how you solved the problem.

1¢ – 1st day
2¢ – 2nd day
4¢ – 3rd day
8¢ – 4th day
16¢ – 5th day
32 – 6th day
64 – 7th day
$1.28 – 8th day
$2.56 – 9th day

$5.12
10th day

She shold get paid by dobles, because the amount already got over $1.00 on the 10th day.

This Level 3 paper illustrates the following features: The work is labeled so that it is possible to see how the earnings accumulate daily. The daily total earned is listed next to each day's new earnings. On Day 7, the total earnings reach $1.26. This total is compared to $1.00 per week earned with the first method. It is implied that if $1.26 (more than $1.00) is earned in the first week, then the grand total will be greater than $4.00.

This Level 3 paper illustrates the following features: The method is labeled "2" lists the earnings that accumulate daily, but there is no indication that the amounts correspond to days. The total for $1 per week is stated and labeled "1." There is a computation error when 64¢ is doubled. The pennies are ignored. The explanation states the answer and describes that by the tenth day, the daily earnings surpass the total earnings from the first method.

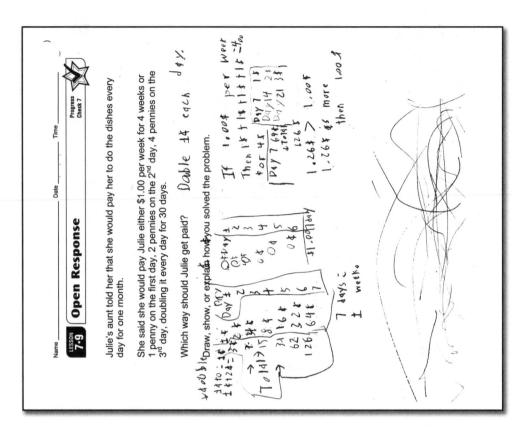

Name _____ Date _____ Time _____

LESSON 7·9

Open Response

Progress Check 7

Julie's aunt told her that she would pay her to do the dishes every day for one month.

She said she would pay Julie either $1.00 per week for 4 weeks or 1 penny on the first day, 2 pennies on the 2nd day, 4 pennies on the 3rd day, doubling it every day for 30 days.

Which way should Julie get paid?

Draw, show, or explain how you solved the problem.

① 1¢ — $2.40
   2¢ — $4.80
   4¢
   8¢
   16¢
   32¢
   64¢
   $1.20   ① $4.00

I am not even on my 30th day but it is overnow much she wold get pad with the first way.

108   Assessment Handbook

This Level 2 paper illustrates the following features: The work is labeled to show how the earnings are calculated daily through Day 7 and weekly through Week 4 according to the two payment methods. The computation is correct for both methods. The explanation appears to compare the total after 7 days with the total for 4 weeks, concluding that the 4-week total is better.

This Level 1 paper illustrates the following features: Both methods are misrepresented. For the weekly payment method, the amount is doubled on Week 2, and then $2.00 is added each subsequent week. Instead of doubling the pennies each day, 2 pennies are added each day for 4 days (the number of weeks listed for the weekly method). The conclusion is that more money is earned at $1.00 per week.

Name _____ Date _____ Time _____

LESSON 7·9 **Open Response**

Progress Check 7

Julie's aunt told her that she would pay her to do the dishes every day for one month.

She said she would pay Julie either $1.00 per week for 4 weeks or 1 penny on the first day, 2 pennies on the 2nd day, 4 pennies on the 3rd day, doubling it every day for 30 days.

Which way should Julie get paid?

Draw, show, or explain how you solved the problem.
She should one $1.00 per week.

1 day 2¢
2 day 4¢
3 day 8¢
4 day 16¢
5 day 32¢
6 day 64¢
7 day 1.28 $

Week 1 1.00
Week 2 1.00
Week 3 1.00
Week 4 1.00
        4.00

She should do that becase she can make more mouhg. If she does it in pennies she will make lesse mouhg.

Name _____ Date _____ Time _____

LESSON 7·9 **Open Response**

Progress Check 7

Julie's aunt told her that she would pay her to do the dishes every day for one month.

She said she would pay Julie either $1.00 per week for 4 weeks or 1 penny on the first day, 2 pennies on the 2nd day, 4 pennies on the 3rd day, doubling it every day for 30 days.

Which way should Julie get paid?

Draw, show, or explain how you solved the problem.

1 $1.00
2 $2.00
3 $4.00
4 $6.00

1¢
2P¢
3P¢
4P¢

I think ist

I think the zookees are better because she could buy some thing with the dolls

Penny Safe book because you dont no what to do with it

Assessment Overview **109**

Assessment Overview

In this unit, children explore fractions of regions and collections of objects, as well as relationships between fractions (less than, equal to, greater than). Use the information in this section to develop your assessment plan for Unit 8.

Ongoing Assessment

Opportunities for using and collecting ongoing assessment information are highlighted in Informing Instruction and Recognizing Student Achievement notes. Student products, along with observations and suggested writing prompts, provide a range of useful assessment information.

Informing Instruction

The Informing Instruction notes highlight children's thinking and point out common misconceptions. Informing Instruction in Unit 8: Lessons 8-1, 8-3, and 8-5.

Recognizing Student Achievement

The Recognizing Student Achievement notes highlight specific tasks from which teachers can collect assessment data to monitor and document children's progress toward meeting Grade-Level Goals.

Lesson	Content Assessed	Where to Find It
8•1	**Model fractions as equal parts of a region and name the fraction.** [Number and Numeration Goal 3]	*TLG,* p. 607
8•2	**Record addition facts.** [Operations and Computation Goal 1]	*TLG,* p. 613
8•3	**Calculate coin combinations.** [Operations and Computation Goal 2]	*TLG,* p. 619
8•4	**Identify the value of digits in numbers.** [Number and Numeration Goal 2]	*TLG,* p. 624
8•5	**Record equivalent fraction pairs.** [Number and Numeration Goal 6]	*TLG,* p. 629
8•6	**Record equivalent units of time.** [Measurement and Reference Frames Goal 3]	*TLG,* p. 634
8•7	**Solve fraction number stories involving fractions of a collection.** [Number and Numeration Goal 3]	*TLG,* p. 638

Math Boxes

Math Boxes, one of several types of tasks highlighted in the Recognizing Student Achievement notes, have an additional useful feature. Math Boxes in most lessons are paired or linked with Math Boxes in one or two other lessons that have similar problems. Paired or linked Math Boxes in Unit 8: 8-1 and 8-3; 8-2, 8-4 and 8-6; and 8-5 and 8-7.

Writing/Reasoning Prompts

In Unit 8, a variety of writing prompts encourage children to explain their strategies and thinking, to reflect on their learning, and to make connections to other mathematics or life experiences. Here are some of the Unit 8 suggestions:

Lesson	Writing/Reasoning Prompts	Where to Find It
8◆1	How did you figure out the *in* number when you only knew the *out* number?	*TLG*, p. 608
8◆2	Explain how you knew how many dots to color green.	*TLG*, p. 614
8◆5	Describe how you found the rules in the Frames-and-Arrows problem.	*TLG*, p. 629

Portfolio Opportunities

Portfolios are a versatile tool for assessment. They help children reflect on their mathematical growth and help teachers understand and document that growth. Each unit identifies several student products that can be selected and stored in a portfolio. Here are some of the Unit 8 suggestions:

Lesson	Portfolio Opportunities	Where to Find It
8◆1	Children explain their strategy for figuring out the *in* number when given the *out* number.	*TLG*, p. 608
8◆2	Children explain how they knew how many dots to color green.	*TLG*, p. 614
8◆3	Children calculate coin combinations.	*TLG*, p. 619
8◆5	Children draw or write a description of how they found rules for Frames-and-Arrows problems.	*TLG*, p. 629
8◆7	Children write and solve fraction number stories to compile in individual books.	*TLG*, p. 639

Periodic Assessment

Every Progress Check lesson includes opportunities to observe children's progress and to collect student products in a variety of ways—Self Assessment, Oral and Slate Assessment, Written Assessment, and an Open Response task. For more details, see the first page of Progress Check 8, Lesson 8-8, page 640, of the *Teacher's Lesson Guide*.

Progress Check Modifications

Written Assessments are one way children demonstrate what they know. The table below shows modifications for the Written Assessment in this unit. Use these to maximize opportunities for children to demonstrate what they know. Modifications can be given individually or written on the board for the class.

Problem(s)	Modifications for Written Assessment
1	For Problem 1, explain why you chose your answer.
9	For Problem 9, take another copy of the pictures, cut them out, and then fold them to find the lines of symmetry.
11	For Problem 11, take square sheets of paper. Fold one in half and a second one into fourths before dividing the pictures into halves and fourths.
12, 13	For Problems 12 and 13, use pennies or counters to solve the problems.

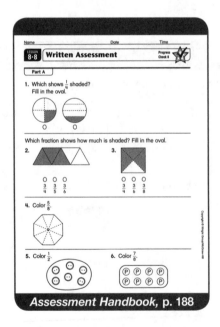

Assessment Handbook, p. 188

The Written Assessment for the Unit 8 Progress Check is on pages 188–190.

Open Response, *Sharing Brownies*

Description

For this task, children share 3 brownies equally among 4 children.

Focus

◆ **Use manipulatives and drawings to model fractions as equal parts of a region.**
[Number and Numeration Goal 3]

◆ **Name the fraction of a region.**
[Number and Numeration Goal 3]

◆ **Use equal grouping to model division.**
[Operations and Computation Goal 4]

Implementation Tips

◆ Review fraction notation, and remind children that the answer should be a fraction.

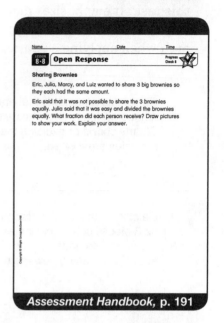

Assessment Handbook, p. 191

Modifications for Meeting Diverse Needs

◆ Provide children with 3 rectangles to model the 3 brownies. Have them first draw their answers on the rectangles and then cut them apart to model the problem.

◆ Have children figure out what fraction of the brownie Luiz would have left if he shared his portion of the brownies with another friend. $\left(\frac{3}{8}\right)$ Remind them that drawing and labeling each part with fractions can help them solve the problem.

Improving Open Response Skills

After children complete the task, have them analyze several examples of written explanations (without the illustrations). Consider using some of the explanations included in the Sample Student Responses beginning on page 115 of this book. Record each explanation on a piece of chart paper and give 1 to each group. Have children identify and record information that is missing from the sample explanation. Have them work together to write a complete list of all of the steps needed to solve the problem.

Note: The wording and formatting of the text on the student samples that follow may vary slightly from the actual task your children will complete. These minor discrepancies will not affect the implementation of the task.

Rubric

This rubric is designed to help you assess levels of mathematical performance on this task. It emphasizes mathematical understanding with only a mention of clarity of explanation. Consider the expectations of standardized tests in your area when applying a rubric. Modify this sample rubric as appropriate.

4 Calculates and states that each person receives $\frac{3}{4}$ of a brownie using fraction notation. Clearly illustrates a strategy for dividing the brownies into equal shares. Clearly shows or explains the steps in the solution strategy, including how the brownies are divided.

3 Calculates that each person receives $\frac{3}{4}$ of a brownie, but might express the answer as 3 pieces of brownie instead of $\frac{3}{4}$ of a brownie. Illustrates a strategy for dividing the brownies into equal shares. Shows or explains most of the key steps in the solution strategy, including how the brownies are divided or distributed.

2 Divides the brownies into parts that can be distributed equally among 4 children. Illustrates a strategy that indicates some understanding of equal shares. Attempts an explanation that makes some sense in the context of the problem, but it might be incomplete or incorrect.

1 Attempts to divide the brownies among the 4 children. Attempts to illustrate or explain a strategy, but it might be incorrect or provide no evidence of understanding the problem.

0 Does not attempt to understand or solve the problem.

Sample Student Responses

This Level 4 paper illustrates the following features: In the illustration, each brownie is divided into 4 equal pieces. The pieces are labeled with the children's names to show who gets each piece. The answer is written using correct fraction notation. The explanation clearly describes how the brownies are divided into 4 pieces each.

This Level 4 paper illustrates the following features: In the illustration, 2 brownies are divided into halves and the third brownie is divided into fourths. The pieces are labeled with the children's initials to show who gets each piece. The explanation states that each person receives $\frac{1}{2}$ and $\frac{1}{4}$ of a brownie, and clearly describes how the brownies are divided.

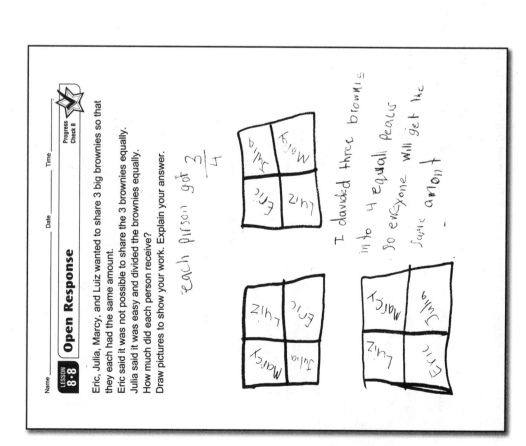

This Level 3 paper illustrates the following features: In the illustration, each brownie is divided into 4 equal pieces. The pieces are labeled with the children's initials to show who gets each piece. There is a smaller illustration showing 4 circles (representing the children) with 3 pieces of brownie drawn above each circle. The explanation states that each person receives 3 pieces of brownie.

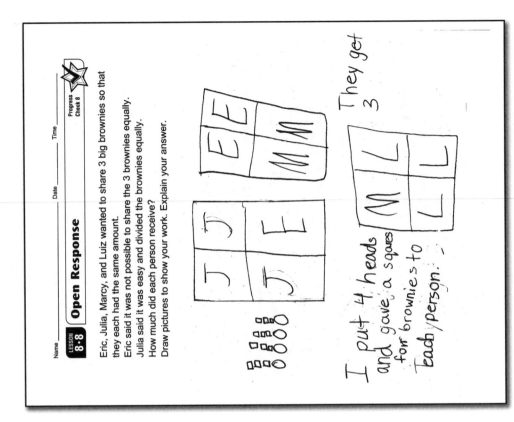

LESSON
8·8 **Open Response**

Progress
Check 8

Eric, Julia, Marcy, and Luiz wanted to share 3 big brownies so that they each had the same amount.
Eric said it was not possible to share the 3 brownies equally.
Julia said it was easy and divided the brownies equally.
How much did each person receive?
Draw pictures to show your work. Explain your answer.

I put 4 heads and gave a sqaes for brownies to each/person.

They get 3

This Level 3 paper illustrates the following features: In the illustration, each brownie is divided into 4 equal pieces. The pieces are labeled with the numbers 1–4 and lines are drawn connecting pictures of 4 children with the 3 pieces of brownies each child gets. The answer is written using correct fraction notation. The explanation states that each person receives three $\frac{1}{4}$-pieces of a brownie.

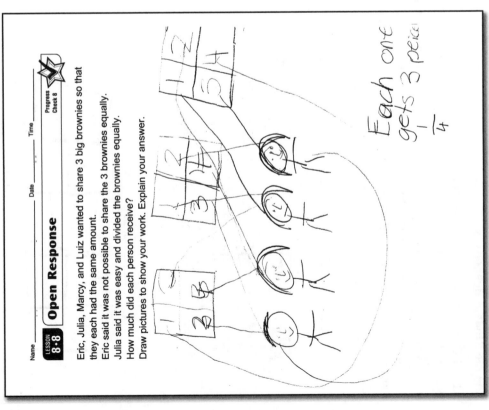

LESSON
8·8 **Open Response**

Progress
Check 8

Eric, Julia, Marcy, and Luiz wanted to share 3 big brownies so that they each had the same amount.
Eric said it was not possible to share the 3 brownies equally.
Julia said it was easy and divided the brownies equally.
How much did each person receive?
Draw pictures to show your work. Explain your answer.

Each one gets $\frac{1}{4}$ pieces

This Level 1 paper illustrates the following features: In the illustration, 2 brownies are divided into halves and the third brownie is divided into $4\frac{1}{5}$-pieces and $4\frac{1}{20}$-pieces. The answer given is that each person receives 1 piece.

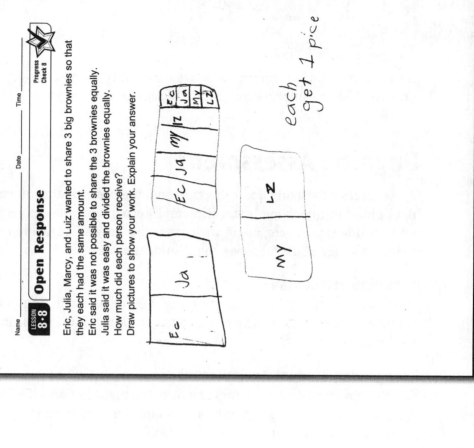

This Level 2 paper illustrates the following features: In the illustration, 2 brownies are divided into halves and the third brownie is divided into fourths. Lines are drawn connecting each of the 4 children with $\frac{1}{2}$ of a brownie and $\frac{1}{4}$ of a brownie. The answer given is that each person receives 2 pieces without explaining that the pieces represent different fractions of a brownie.

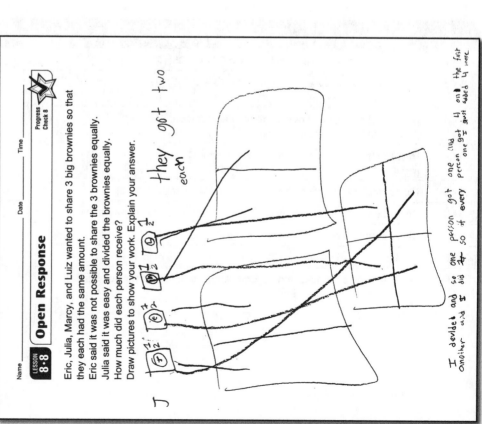

Unit 9

Assessment Overview

In this unit, children explore measurement concepts in a variety of everyday contexts. Use the information in this section to develop your assessment plan for Unit 9.

Ongoing Assessment

Opportunities for using and collecting ongoing assessment information are highlighted in Informing Instruction and Recognizing Student Achievement notes. Student products, along with observations and suggested writing prompts, provide a range of useful assessment information.

Informing Instruction

The Informing Instruction notes highlight children's thinking and point out common misconceptions. Informing Instruction in Unit 9: Lessons 9-1, 9-3, 9-4, 9-7, and 9-8.

Recognizing Student Achievement

The Recognizing Student Achievement notes highlight specific tasks from which teachers can collect assessment data to monitor and document children's progress toward meeting Grade-Level Goals.

Lesson	Content Assessed	Where to Find It
9•1	Find the modes for data sets. [Data and Chance Goal 2]	*TLG*, p. 661
9•2	Use a ruler to measure the lengths of objects. [Measurement and Reference Frames Goal 1]	*TLG*, p. 669
9•3	Measure the lengths of objects to the nearest inch. [Measurement and Reference Frames Goal 1]	*TLG*, p. 675
9•4	Measure the sides of a rectangle to the nearest inch. [Measurement and Reference Frames Goal 1]	*TLG*, p. 681
9•5	Find a fraction of a collection. [Number and Numeration Goal 3]	*TLG*, p. 684
9•6	Record addition and subtraction facts. [Operations and Computation Goal 1]	*TLG*, p. 692
9•7	Share counters equally. [Operations and Computation Goal 4]	*TLG*, p. 697
9•8	Continue numeric patterns. [Patterns, Functions, and Algebra Goal 1]	*TLG*, p. 702
9•9	Write number sentences and generate equivalent names for numbers. [Number and Numeration Goal 5]	*TLG*, p. 708

Math Boxes

Math Boxes, one of several types of tasks highlighted in the Recognizing Student Achievement notes, have an additional useful feature. Math Boxes in most lessons are paired or linked with Math Boxes in one or two other lessons that have similar problems. Paired or linked Math Boxes in Unit 9: 9-1 and 9-3; 9-2 and 9-4; 9-5, 9-7 and 9-9; and 9-6 and 9-8.

Writing/Reasoning Prompts

In Unit 9, a variety of writing prompts encourage children to explain their strategies and thinking, to reflect on their learning, and to make connections to other mathematics or life experiences. Here are some of the Unit 9 suggestions:

Lesson	Writing/Reasoning Prompts	Where to Find It
9◆1	Explain how you found the median.	*TLG*, p. 664
9◆4	Explain how you know what numbers to fill in on the number grid.	*TLG*, p. 681
9◆6	Describe how you determined the perimeter of the rectangle.	*TLG*, p. 692
9◆7	Explain how you figured out if you had enough money to buy the chips.	*TLG*, p. 697

Portfolio Opportunities

Portfolios are a versatile tool for assessment. They help children reflect on their mathematical growth and help teachers understand and document that growth. Each unit identifies several student products that can be selected and stored in a portfolio. Here are some of the Unit 9 suggestions:

Lesson	Portfolio Opportunities	Where to Find It
9◆1	Children explain how to find the median.	*TLG*, p. 664
9◆6	Children explain how to find the perimeter of a rectangle.	*TLG*, p. 692
9◆7	Children explain how they know if there is enough money to buy the chips.	*TLG*, p. 697
9◆9	Children write number sentences and generate equivalent names for numbers.	*TLG*, p. 708

Periodic Assessment

Every Progress Check lesson includes opportunities to observe children's progress and to collect student products in a variety of ways—Self Assessment, Oral and Slate Assessment, Written Assessment, and an Open Response task. For more details, see the first page of Progress Check 9, Lesson 9-10, page 710, of the *Teacher's Lesson Guide*.

Progress Check Modifications

Written Assessments are one way children demonstrate what they know. The table below shows modifications for the Written Assessment in this unit. Use these to maximize opportunities for children to demonstrate what they know. Modifications can be given individually or written on the board for the class.

Problem(s)	Modifications for Written Assessment
1, 2, 13	For Problems 1, 2, and 13, use an inch-only ruler when measuring to the nearest inch and a cm-only ruler when measuring to the nearest cm.
7, 8	For Problems 7 and 8, for each set of numbers, write the individual numbers on stick-on notes, and arrange the stick-on notes in order before finding the landmarks.
9–12	For Problems 9–12, use a number grid to solve the problems.
14	For Problem 14, explain how you can find many other names for $\frac{1}{2}$.

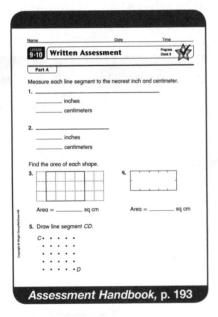

Assessment Handbook, p. 193

The Written Assessment for the Unit 9 Progress Check is on pages 193–194.

Open Response, *A Broken Ruler Problem*

Description

For this task, children figure out how many popsicle sticks of a given length are needed to make a frame of specified dimensions.

Focus

◆ **Use repeated addition and skip counting to model multiplication.**
[Operations and Computation Goal 4]

◆ **Measure length to the nearest inch.**
[Measurement and Reference Frames Goal 1]

Implementation Tips

◆ Provide rulers and popsicle or craft sticks for children to model the problem.

Modifications for Meeting Diverse Needs

◆ Provide children with 5-inch strips of paper to model the popsicle sticks in the problem. Have them measure one strip to determine the length of a popsicle stick and draw the frame to scale on a piece of chart paper. Then have children use paper strips to build the frame. Children can line up the strips they used and find the total length of the sticks.

◆ Victor's friend Julie said the popsicle stick is 11 inches long. What mistake did she make?

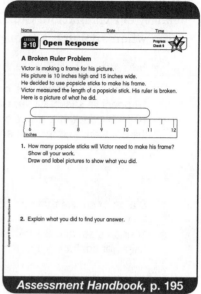

Assessment Handbook, p. 195

Improving Open Response Skills

Before children begin the task, read the task together. Have children discuss what they know, what they need to find out, and make a list of the group's contributions. Post this list during the task implementation.

Note: The wording and formatting of the text on the student samples that follow may vary slightly from the actual task your children will complete. These minor discrepancies will not affect the implementation of the task.

Rubric

This rubric is designed to help you assess levels of mathematical performance on this task. It emphasizes mathematical understanding with only a mention of clarity of explanation. Consider the expectations of standardized tests in your area when applying a rubric. Modify this sample rubric as appropriate.

4 States or shows that one popsicle stick is 5 inches long and that Victor needs 10 popsicle sticks. Clearly illustrates or explains that Victor needs 2 sticks on each 10-inch side and 3 sticks on each 15-inch side. Clearly explains the steps for finding the solution, and the explanation describes the solution illustrated in Problem 1.

3 States or shows that one popsicle stick is 5 inches long and that Victor needs 10 popsicle sticks. Clearly illustrates or explains that Victor needs 2 sticks on each 10-inch side, and 3 sticks on each 15-inch side. The explanation might be difficult to follow or confusing, but it is clearly related to the solution illustrated in Problem 1.

2 States or shows that Victor needs 10 popsicle sticks. Illustrates or explains that Victor needs 2 sticks on one side and 3 sticks on the other side. The explanation might be incomplete, or it might not describe the work illustrated in Problem 1.

1 Attempts to solve and illustrate the problem, but there might be little evidence of understanding the context of the problem. The explanation might be missing or incorrect.

0 Does not attempt to understand or solve the problem.

Sample Student Responses

This Level 4 paper illustrates the following features: It is determined that Victor needs 10 popsicle sticks. The drawing is labeled with the total dimensions in inches. The explanation describes all the steps for finding a solution, including measuring the stick and comparing its length to the length and width of the frame. There are 2 multiplication number models used to show how the number of sticks for each dimension is found.

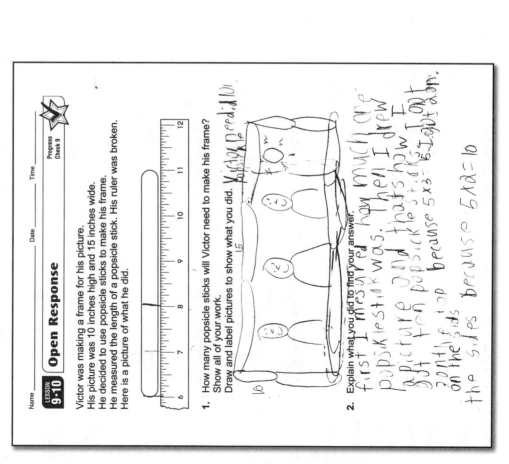

This Level 4 paper illustrates the following features: The popsicle stick is labeled with a length of 5. It is determined that Victor needs 10 popsicle sticks. The dimensions of the frame in the drawing are labeled in inches and in number of popsicle sticks. The explanation describes all the steps for finding a solution, including measuring the stick and using repeated addition to determine how many sticks are needed for each dimension of the frame.

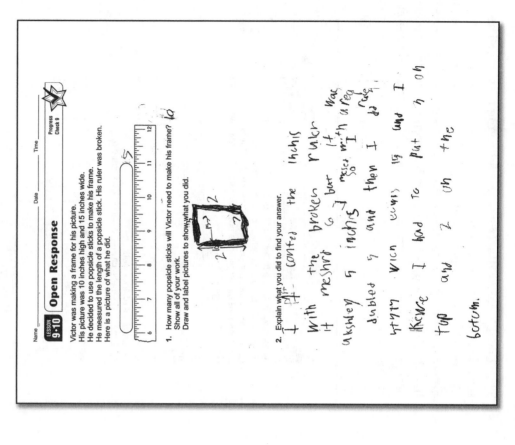

This Level 3 paper illustrates the following features: The popsicle stick is labeled with 5 inches as its length. It is determined that Victor needs 10 popsicle sticks. The drawing is labeled on one dimension and a rectangle is illustrated with both dimensions listed. The explanation describes how repeated addition is used to determine the number of sticks needed for each dimension of the frame.

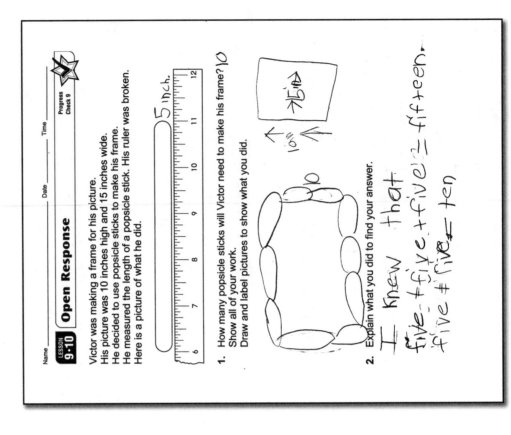

This Level 3 paper illustrates the following features: The popsicle stick is marked off into 5 1-inch segments. It is determined that Victor needs 10 popsicle sticks. The drawing is not labeled. The explanation describes the steps for finding a solution including measuring the stick and using repeated addition to determine how many sticks are needed for each dimension of the frame. The explanation describing how the broken ruler is used to measure the stick is confusing.

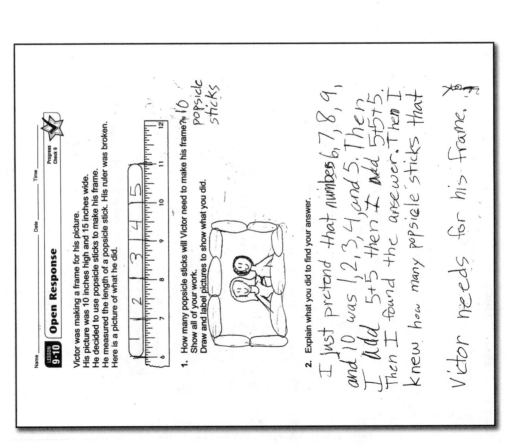

This Level 2 paper illustrates the following features: It is determined that Victor needs 10 popsicle sticks. The drawing is not labeled but the 10 popsicle sticks are represented. The explanation attempts to describe how repeated addition is used to determine the number of sticks for each dimension of the frame. However, all of the individual stick lengths are added together for a grand total of 50.

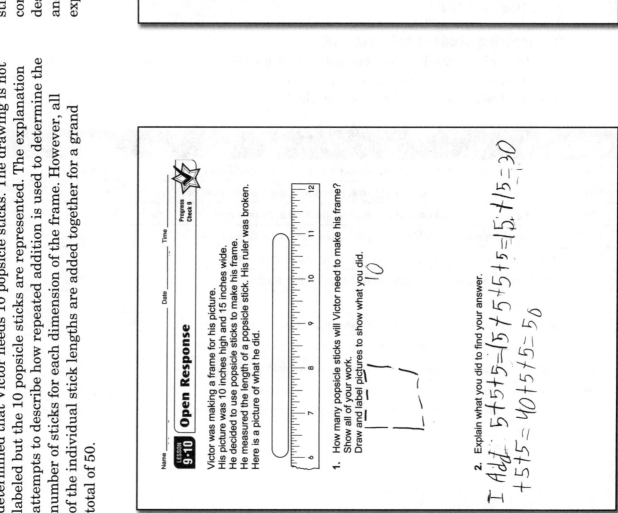

Name _____ Date _____ Time _____

LESSON 9·10 **Open Response** Progress Check 9

Victor was making a frame for his picture.
His picture was 10 inches high and 15 inches wide.
He decided to use popsicle sticks to make his frame.
He measured the length of a popsicle stick. His ruler was broken.
Here is a picture of what did.

1. How many popsicle sticks will Victor need to make his frame?
Show all of your work.
Draw and label pictures to show what you did.

10

2. Explain what you did to find your answer.
I Add 5+5+5=15+5+5+5+5=15+5+5=30
+5+5= 40+5+5=50

This Level 1 paper illustrates the following features: The popsicle stick appears to be labeled with a length of 5. The drawing is correct but there are no labels. The explanation attempts to describe the steps used to figure out the length of the popsicle stick and then measure around the picture with the popsicle stick. The explanation does not state what is being measured.

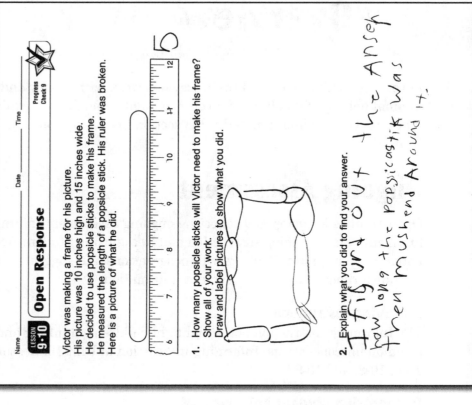

Name _____ Date _____ Time _____

LESSON 9·10 **Open Response** Progress Check 9

Victor was making a frame for his picture.
His picture was 10 inches high and 15 inches wide.
He decided to use popsicle sticks to make his frame.
He measured the length of a popsicle stick. His ruler was broken.
Here is a picture of what he did.

5

1. How many popsicle sticks will Victor need to make his frame?
Show all of your work.
Draw and label pictures to show what you did.

2. Explain what you did to find your answer.
I figurd out the Ansek
how long the popsicostik was
then I mushend Around it.

Assessment Overview

In this unit, children extend their previous work with money and fractions to decimal notation for dollars-and-cents amounts, and further explore place-value concepts. Use the information in this section to develop your assessment plan for Unit 10.

Ongoing Assessment

Opportunities for using and collecting ongoing assessment information are highlighted in Informing Instruction and Recognizing Student Achievement notes. Student products, along with observations and suggested writing prompts, provide a range of useful assessment information.

Informing Instruction

The Informing Instruction notes highlight children's thinking and point out common misconceptions. Informing Instruction in Unit 10: Lessons 10-3, 10-5, 10-6, 10-8, and 10-9.

Recognizing Student Achievement

The Recognizing Student Achievement notes highlight specific tasks from which teachers can collect assessment data to monitor and document children's progress toward meeting Grade-Level Goals.

Lesson	Content Assessed	Where to Find It
10◆1	**Calculate coin and bill combinations.** [Operations and Computation Goal 2]	*TLG*, p. 728
10◆2	**Estimate the combined value of two items.** [Operations and Computation Goal 3]	*TLG*, p. 732
10◆3	**Model fractions as equal parts of a collection.** [Number and Numeration Goal 3]	*TLG*, p. 741
10◆4	**Calculate coin and bill combinations.** [Operations and Computation Goal 2]	*TLG*, p. 746
10◆5	**Identify a rule for a function.** [Patterns, Functions, and Algebra Goal 1]	*TLG*, p. 751
10◆6	**Read the temperature.** [Measurement and Reference Frames Goal 5]	*TLG*, p. 756
10◆7	**Record addition facts.** [Operations and Computation Goal 1]	*TLG*, p. 761
10◆8	**Estimate the amount of change from a transaction.** [Operations and Computation Goal 3]	*TLG*, p. 765
10◆9	**Convert between units of time.** [Measurement and Reference Frame Goal 3]	*TLG*, p. 774
10◆10	**Identify the value of digits.** [Number and Numeration Goal 2]	*TLG*, p. 777
10◆11	**Identify fractions of a collection.** [Number and Numeration Goal 3]	*TLG*, p. 782

Math Boxes

Math Boxes, one of several types of tasks highlighted in the Recognizing Student Achievement notes, have an additional useful feature. Math Boxes in most lessons are paired or linked with Math Boxes in one or two other lessons that have similar problems. Paired or linked Math Boxes in Unit 10: 10-1, 10-3, and 10-5; 10-2 and 10-4; 10-6, 10-8, and 10-10; and 10-7, 10-9, and 10-11.

Writing/Reasoning Prompts

In Unit 10, a variety of writing prompts encourage children to explain their strategies and thinking, to reflect on their learning, and to make connections to other mathematics or life experiences. Here are some of the Unit 10 suggestions:

Lesson	Writing/Reasoning Prompts	Where to Find It
10◆3	Explain what you notice about the number of nickels and the number of dimes.	*TLG*, p. 741
10◆4	Describe how you found the median.	*TLG*, p. 746
10◆6	Explain what the temperature would be if it were 20°F warmer, and show your work.	*TLG*, p. 756
10◆9	Make up a "What's My Rule?" table using 3 feet = 1 yard as the rule.	*TLG*, p. 773
10◆10	Explain how you found the correct amount of change.	*TLG*, p. 778

Portfolio Opportunities

Portfolios are a versatile tool for assessment. They help children reflect on their mathematical growth and help teachers understand and document that growth. Each unit identifies several student products that can be selected and stored in a portfolio. Here are some of the Unit 10 suggestions:

Lesson	Portfolio Opportunities	Where to Find It
10◆3	Children explain what they notice about the relationship between the number of nickels and the number of dimes in $3.00.	*TLG*, p. 741
10◆4	Children describe how they found the median.	*TLG*, p. 746
10◆6	Children explain what the temperature would be if it were 20°F warmer.	*TLG*, p. 756
10◆7	Children work with partners to practice addition and subtraction facts and record the facts they know.	*TLG*, p. 761

Periodic Assessment

Every Progress Check lesson includes opportunities to observe children's progress and to collect student products in a variety of ways—Self Assessment, Oral and Slate Assessment, Written Assessment, and an Open Response task. For more details, see the first page of Progress Check 10, Lesson 10-12, page 784 of the *Teacher's Lesson Guide*.

Progress Check Modifications

Written Assessments are one way children demonstrate what they know. The table below shows modifications for the Written Assessment in this unit. Use these to maximize opportunities for children to demonstrate what they know. Modifications can be given individually or written on the board for the class.

Problem(s)	Modifications for Written Assessment
3, 4	For Problems 3 and 4, label the 4 longer marks between the multiples of 10 on either side of the number of degrees you are using in the problem.
5	For Problem 5, write two of your own pairs of *in* and *out* numbers.
11, 12	For Problems 11 and 12, use tool-kit coins and bills to solve the problems.
13	For Problem 13, use 3 quarter-sheets of paper to represent the people and 12 counters to represent the marbles.

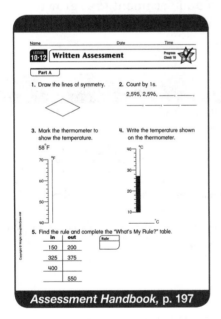

Assessment Handbook, p. 197

The Written Assessment for the Unit 10 Progress Check is on pages 197–199.

Open Response, *Comparing Coins*

Description

For this task, children figure out coin combinations based on a series of clues, including one person having double what the other has.

Focus

◆ **Write money amounts in dollars-and-cents notation.** [Number and Numeration Goal 2]
◆ **Model equivalent names for $\frac{1}{2}$.** [Number and Numeration Goal 6]
◆ **Make exchanges between coins.** [Measurement and Reference Frames Goal 4]

Implementation Tips

◆ Review the meaning of *twice as much*. Have volunteers share a few simple examples.
◆ Provide tool-kit coins, including only four quarters, for children to model the problem.

Assessment Handbook, p. 200

Modifications for Meeting Diverse Needs

◆ Provide children with a half-sheet of paper labeled *Sue,* which has 5 circles drawn on it to represent her coins. Provide them with another half-sheet of paper labeled *Julian* with 10 circles drawn on it. Have children put tool-kit coins in the circles to model their solutions. When they have solved the problem, have them record their work on the master.
◆ Have children find a second coin combination for Julian that makes the problem true and explain how they found the solution.

Improving Open Response Skills

Before children begin the task, read the problem together. Have children identify the important information contained in the problem. Have them organize their thoughts according to what they know about Julian's and Sue's coins. Have children write parallel statements for Julian and Sue whenever possible. For example, if Sue's coins are worth twice as much as Julian's, then Julian's coins are worth half as much as Sue's. Keep this list posted during the task, and have children check their solutions against the list to be sure each statement is true.

Note: The wording and formatting of the text on the student samples that follow may vary slightly from the actual task your children will complete. These minor discrepancies will not affect the implementation of the task.

Rubric

This rubric is designed to help you assess levels of mathematical performance on this task. It emphasizes mathematical understanding with only a mention of clarity of explanation. Consider the expectations of standardized tests in your area when applying a rubric. Modify this sample rubric as appropriate.

4 Uses the specified coins to record coin combinations with 10 coins for Julian and 5 coins for Sue. Julian's 10 coins are worth $0.55 and Sue's 5 coins are worth $1.10. The explanation provides evidence of reasoning about why Sue has the quarters as well as about the relationship between Sue's and Julian's totals. Clearly explains the solution steps.

3 Uses the specified coins to record coin combinations with 10 coins for Julian and 5 coins for Sue. Julian's 10 coins are worth $0.55 and Sue's 5 coins are worth $1.10. Explains some of the solution, steps but might not include reasoning for the steps.

2 Might use the specified coins but there might be errors. Draws coins to match the given total. Chooses total amounts so that Sue's total is more than Julian's. Might attempt to explain some of the solution steps, but the explanation might be incomplete.

1 Draws coin combinations for Julian and Sue. Calculates the total of the coin combinations, but there might be calculation errors. Might explain some of the solution steps, but the explanation might make no sense in the context of the problem.

0 Does not attempt to solve the problem.

Sample Student Responses

This Level 4 paper illustrates the coin combinations drawn correctly with Julian having 9 nickels and 1 dime, while Sue has 4 quarters and 1 dime. The coin combinations are totaled correctly. The explanation includes reasoning about why Sue must have an even total if Julian has exactly half as much.

This Level 4 paper illustrates the coin combinations drawn correctly with Julian having 5 dimes and 5 pennies, while Sue has 4 quarters and 1 dime. The coin combinations are totaled correctly. The explanation includes reasoning about why Sue must have 4 quarters—because she has more than $1—and why Sue must have an even total if Julian has exactly half as much.

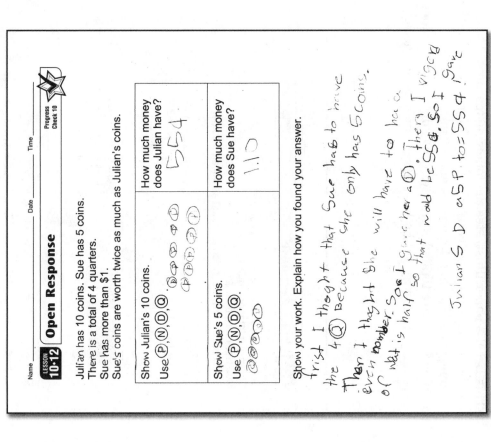

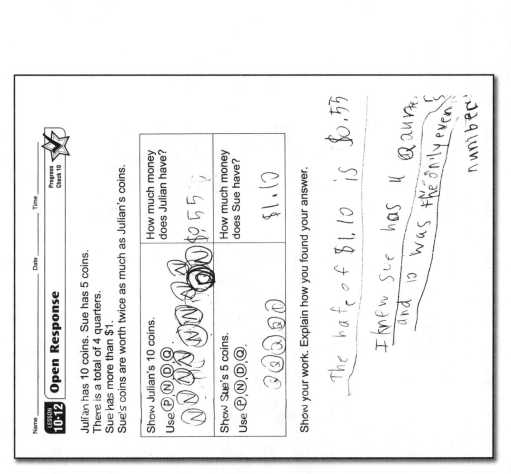

This Level 3 paper illustrates the following features. The coin combinations are drawn correctly with Julian having 9 nickels and 1 dime, while Sue has 4 quarters and 1 dime. The coin combinations are totaled correctly. The explanation includes reasoning about why Julian has half as much as Sue does.

LESSON 10-12 Open Response
Progress Check 10

Julian has 10 coins. Sue has 5 coins.
There is a total of 4 quarters.
Sue has more than $1.
Sue's coins are worth twice as much as Julian's coins.

Show Julian's 10 coins. Use P, N, D, Q. N N N N N N N N N D	How much money does Julian have? $0.55
Show Sue's 5 coins. Use P, N, D, Q. Q Q Q Q D	How much money does Sue have? $1.10

Show your work. Explain how you found your answer.
1 We figyed out all the coins sue had.
2 We cut see coins in haf.
3 We kpw that Julian had hafe as much as Sue did. Julian had 55¢
4 Then we fund out the 10 coin Julian had
5 Then we wrot how I figrd in out.

This Level 3 paper illustrates the following features. The coin combinations are drawn correctly with Julian having 9 nickels and 1 dime, while Sue has 4 quarters and 1 dime. The coin combinations are totaled correctly. The explanation simply restates the recorded coin combination with no reasoning explained.

LESSON 10-12 Open Response
Progress Check 10

Julian has 10 coins. Sue has 5 coins.
There is a total of 4 quarters.
Sue has more than $1.
Sue's coins are worth twice as much as Julian's coins.

Show Julian's 10 coins. Use P, N, D, Q. N N N N N N N N N D	How much money does Julian have? 55¢
Show Sue's 5 coins. Use P, N, D, Q. Q Q Q Q D	How much money does Sue have? $1.10

Show your work. Explain how you found your answer.
I gave Sue all the 4 @'s, then I goosa @ to eaqul $1.10. Then I gave Julian 9@'s, then I gave one @ to eaqul 55¢. Then I add it again to make sher.

This Level 1 paper illustrates 10 coins are drawn for Julian and Sue's coins are worth twice as much as Julian's. The totals are correct for the coins drawn, but some requirements of the problem were ignored.

This Level 2 paper illustrates the correct amount is drawn for each child, but the coin combinations require more than 4 quarters. The explanation appears to describe how to check and be sure that Sue has twice as much as Julian.

Name _____ Date _____ Time _____

LESSON 10·12 Open Response

Julian has 10 coins. Sue has 5 coins.
There is a total of 4 quarters.
Sue has more than $1.
Sue's coins are worth twice as much as Julian's coins.

Show Julian's 10 coins. Use Ⓟ, Ⓝ, Ⓓ, Ⓠ. Ⓟ Ⓟ Ⓟ Ⓟ Ⓟ Ⓟ Ⓟ Ⓟ Ⓟ Ⓟ	How much money does Julian have? 10¢
Show Sue's 5 coins. Use Ⓟ, Ⓝ, Ⓓ, Ⓠ. Ⓟ Ⓟ	How much money does Sue have? 20¢

Show your work. Explain how you found your answer.

◯◯◯◯ ◯◯◯◯ ◯◯◯

◯◯◯ ◯◯◯◯ ◯◯ ◯◯◯

I did duble 10¢ together
and I get the answer. That's
how I did the problme.

Name _____ Date _____ Time _____

LESSON 10·12 Open Response

Julian has 10 coins. Sue has 5 coins.
There is a total of 4 quarters.
Sue has more than $1.
Sue's coins are worth twice as much as Julian's coins.

Show Julian's 10 coins. Use Ⓟ, Ⓝ, Ⓓ, Ⓠ. 5 Ⓟ Ⓠ Ⓓ 3 Ⓝ	How much money does Julian have? 55¢
Show Sue's 5 coins. Use Ⓟ, Ⓝ, Ⓓ, Ⓠ. 4 Ⓠ Ⓓ	How much money does Sue have? $1.10

Show your work. Explain how you found your answer.

you just add 55 and they're goes your
answer.

$\frac{55}{110}$

Assessment Overview

In this unit, children extend their work with addition and subtraction to include decimals in the context of money, and further explore multiplication and division. Use the information in this section to develop your assessment plan for Unit 11.

Ongoing Assessment

Opportunities for using and collecting ongoing assessment information are highlighted in Informing Instruction and Recognizing Student Achievement notes. Student products, along with observations and suggested writing prompts, provide a range of useful assessment information.

Informing Instruction

The Informing Instruction notes highlight children's thinking and point out common misconceptions. Informing Instruction in Unit 11: Lessons 11-2, 11-3, and 11-9.

Recognizing Student Achievement

The Recognizing Student Achievement notes highlight specific tasks from which teachers can collect assessment data to monitor and document children's progress toward meeting Grade-Level Goals.

Lesson	Content Assessed	Where to Find It
11•1	Find differences between multidigit numbers. [Operations and Computation Goal 2]	*TLG*, p. 805
11•2	Tell time to the nearest 5 minutes. [Measurement and Reference Frames Goal 6]	*TLG*, p. 808
11•3	Solve multidigit subtraction problems. [Operations and Computation Goal 2]	*TLG*, p. 813
11•4	Solve a multiplication problem using an equal groups model. [Operations and Computation Goal 4]	*TLG*, p. 819
11•5	Solve a division problem using an equal sharing model. [Operations and Computation Goal 4]	*TLG*, p. 825
11•6	Draw arrays for multiplication facts. [Operations and Computation Goal 4]	*TLG*, p. 833
11•7	Draw sides of a rectangle to the nearest inch. [Measurement and Reference Frames Goal 1]	*TLG*, p. 838
11•8	Find the median of a set of data. [Data and Chance Goal 2]	*TLG*, p. 844
11•9	Estimate to solve addition problems with money. [Operations and Computation Goal 3]	*TLG*, p. 847

Math Boxes

Math Boxes, one of several types of tasks highlighted in the Recognizing Student Achievement notes, have an additional useful feature. Math Boxes in most lessons are paired or linked with Math Boxes in one or two other lessons that have similar problems. Paired or linked Math Boxes in Unit 11: 11-1 and 11-3; 11-2 and 11-4; 11-5, 11-7, and 11-9; and 11-6 and 11-8.

Writing/Reasoning Prompts

In Unit 11, a variety of writing prompts encourage children to explain their strategies and thinking, to reflect on their learning, and to make connections to other mathematics or life experiences. Here are some of the Unit 11 suggestions:

Lesson	Writing/Reasoning Prompts	Where to Find It
11◆1	Explain how you found the correct amount of change.	*TLG*, p. 805
11◆4	Describe how you divided the baseball cards equally.	*TLG*, p. 822
11◆6	Describe how you found $\frac{1}{2}$ of the counters.	*TLG*, p. 833
11◆9	Explain how you solved the equal groups problem.	*TLG*, p. 848

Portfolio Opportunities

Portfolios are a versatile tool for assessment. They help children reflect on their mathematical growth and help teachers understand and document that growth. Each unit identifies several student products that can be selected and stored in a portfolio. Here are some of the Unit 11 suggestions:

Lesson	Portfolio Opportunities	Where to Find It
11◆2	Children tell time to the nearest 5 minutes.	*TLG*, p. 808
11◆4	Children use repeated addition, arrays, or skip counting to model multiplication.	*TLG*, p. 819
11◆5	Children solve equal sharing problems.	*TLG*, p. 825
11◆8	Children compare addition/subtraction Fact Triangles to multiplication/division Fact Triangles and describe their observations.	*TLG*, p. 845

Periodic Assessment

Every Progress Check lesson includes opportunities to observe children's progress and to collect student products in a variety of ways—Self Assessment, Oral and Slate Assessment, Written Assessment, and an Open Response task. For more details, see the first page of Progress Check 11, Lesson 11-10, page 850, of the *Teacher's Lesson Guide*.

Progress Check Modifications

Written Assessments are one way children demonstrate what they know. The table below shows modifications for the Written Assessment in this unit. Use these to maximize opportunities for children to demonstrate what they know. Modifications can be given individually or written on the board for the class.

Problem(s)	Modifications for Written Assessment
1, 2	For Problems 1 and 2, use bills and coins to solve the problems.
4–6	For Problems 4–6, use counters to build the arrays before drawing them.
9	For Problem 9, explain how you can compare $\frac{2}{6}$ and $\frac{1}{2}$ without using a picture.
13, 14	For Problems 13 and 14, use the *Money-Exchange Game* place-value mat to organize your work.

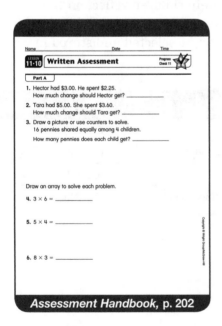

Assessment Handbook, p. 202

The Written Assessment for the Unit 11 Progress Check is on pages 202–204.

Open Response, *Sharing Candy*

30-40 Min.

Description

For this task, children figure out how many pieces of candy are needed so that each of 8 children get an equal number of pieces.

Assessment Handbook, p. 205

Focus

◆ **Use equal sharing and equal grouping to model division.**
[Operations and Computation Goal 4]

Implementation Tips

◆ Provide counters for children to model the problem.

Modifications for Meeting Diverse Needs

◆ Provide 25 counters of 1 color and 8 quarter-sheets of paper. Have children model the problem by distributing the counters (candy) to the 8 quarter-sheets of paper (children). Once they have distributed the 25 counters, have them add counters of a different color until all children have an equal amount. Have children record their work in pictures, words, and numbers.

◆ Have children find a second solution to the problem and have them explain how they could find more solutions to the problem. (*Sample answer: First, you add seven more pieces, but every time you add eight more after that, all of the children will have the same number of pieces.*)

Improving Open Response Skills

After children complete the task, have them organize their answers into two columns on a separate sheet of paper—WHAT they did for each step and WHY they did each step. Have them attach this organization to their original task. Remind children that when they explain their answers, the explanation should include both parts.

Note: The wording and formatting of the text on the student samples that follow may vary slightly from the actual task your children will complete. These minor discrepancies will not affect the implementation of the task.

Rubric

This rubric is designed to help you assess levels of mathematical performance on this task. It emphasizes mathematical understanding with only a mention of clarity of explanation. Consider the expectations of standardized tests in your area when applying a rubric. Modify this sample rubric as appropriate.

4	Specifies how many pieces must be added in order to distribute the candy evenly. Clearly illustrates and explains the strategy. Attempts to record a number sentence used to solve the problem, but there might be minor errors in the notation.
3	Specifies how many pieces must be added in order to distribute the candy evenly. Illustrates the solution to the problem and might restate the answer in words. Attempts to record a number sentence. It might have errors, but it makes sense in the context of the problem.
2	Specifies how many pieces must be added in order to distribute the candy evenly. Attempts to illustrate the solution but the illustration might be incomplete or confusing. Might attempt to record a number sentence, but it might not relate to the problem or might be incorrect.
1	Might attempt to solve the problem but there is little evidence of understanding the question. Might have an illustration or an explanation in words or numbers, but there might be errors or it might be confusing in the context of the problem.
0	Does not attempt to solve the problem.

Sample Student Responses

This Level 4 paper illustrates the following features: The illustration shows 25 pieces of candy distributed among 8 children, and the necessary pieces are added and labeled. The answer is clearly marked. The explanation refers to a division strategy. The number sentence is correct and can be used in solving the problem.

This Level 4 paper illustrates the following features: The illustration shows counting off by 8s (3 times) with one left over. If the pattern were continued, it is clear there would be 7 more. The answer is stated, and the explanation includes a description of the process. The number sentence is correct and can be used in solving the problem.

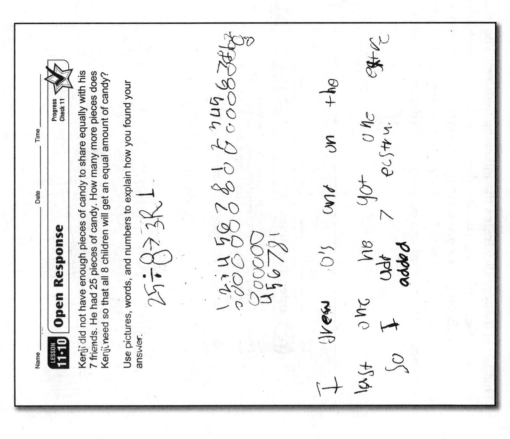

This Level 3 paper illustrates the following features: The illustration shows 40 pieces of candy (tallies) distributed among 8 children and necessary pieces are added to the original 25 to give each child 5 pieces. Fifteen pieces are added to the original 25 to give each child 5 pieces. The answer is clearly stated in words. The number sentence is correct and can be used in solving the problem.

This Level 3 paper illustrates the following features: The illustration shows 25 pieces of candy distributed among 8 children and necessary pieces are added to give each child 4 pieces. The answer is clearly stated in words. The number sentence can be used in solving the problem, but there is an error in the notation.

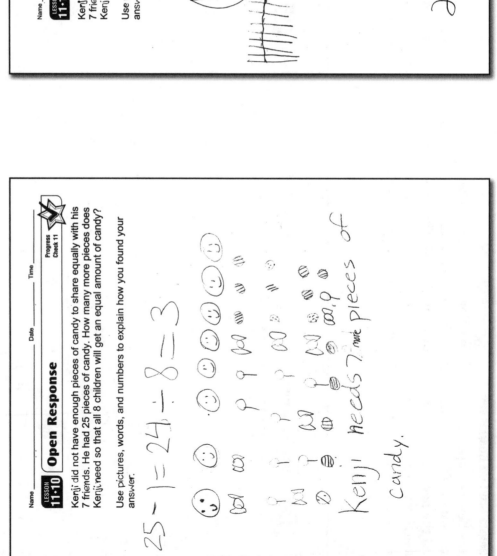

Name _____ Date _____ Time _____

LESSON 11·10   Open Response   Progress Check 11

Kenji did not have enough pieces of candy to share equally with his 7 friends. He had 25 pieces of candy. How many more pieces does Kenji need so that all 8 children will get an equal amount of candy?

Use pictures, words, and numbers to explain how you found your answer.

Kenji needs 15 more pieces of candy

$25 + 15 = 40$ candys.

Name _____ Date _____ Time _____

LESSON 11·10   Open Response   Progress Check 11

Kenji did not have enough pieces of candy to share equally with his 7 friends. He had 25 pieces of candy. How many more pieces does Kenji need so that all 8 children will get an equal amount of candy?

Use pictures, words, and numbers to explain how you found your answer.

$25 - 1 = 24 - 8 = 3$

Kenji needs 7 more pieces of candy.

This Level 1 paper illustrates the following features: There is some correct information, for example, "each kid gets 3 R1." However, there is some confusing information on the page, such as counts by 5s and by 2s. There is a variety of number sentences, but only some of them relate to the context of the problem. The answer is correct, but there are some errors on the page.

Name _____ Date _____ Time _____

LESSON 11·10 **Open Response**

Progress
Check 11

Kenji did not have enough pieces of candy to share equally with his 7 friends. He had 25 pieces of candy. How many more pieces does Kenji need so that all 8 children will get an equal amount of candy?

Use pictures, words, and numbers to explain how you found your answer.

25 - 8

5 10 15 20 25

2, 4, 6, 8, 10, 12, 14, 16, 18, 20, 22, 24

each kid gets 3 R1

3 + 3 + 3 = 9   3 + 3 + 3 = 9 7
3

25 ÷ 8 = 4R0   3 + 3 + 1 7 each peice
                is 50¢
                each kid has
                4 peices of
                candy

kenji has
to buy 7 moe
peices of candy

This Level 2 paper illustrates the following features: The illustration shows 25 pieces of candy (tallies) distributed among 8 children (circles) with 1 left over, but the solution is not explained. The answer is clearly stated in words but there is no number sentence.

Name _____ Date _____ Time _____

LESSON 11·10 **Open Response**

Progress
Check 11

Kenji did not have enough pieces of candy to share equally with his 7 friends. He had 25 pieces of candy. How many more pieces does Kenji need so that all 8 children will get an equal amount of candy?

Use pictures, words, and numbers to explain how you found your answer.

卌卌卌卌卌卌卌卌卌卌卌 l

 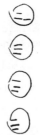 (II) (III) (II) (III) (III) (III) (III) (II)

Kehji need 7 mor candy.

Assessment Overview

In this unit, children review and extend time measurements, mental and algorithmic computation, and data representation and interpretation. Use the information in this section to develop your assessment plan for Unit 12.

Ongoing Assessment

Opportunities for using and collecting ongoing assessment information are highlighted in Informing Instruction and Recognizing Student Achievement notes. Student products, along with observations and suggested writing prompts, provide a range of useful assessment information.

Informing Instruction

The Informing Instruction notes highlight children's thinking and point out common misconceptions. Informing Instruction in Unit 12: Lessons 12-3, 12-4, and 12-7.

Recognizing Student Achievement

The Recognizing Student Achievement notes highlight specific tasks from which teachers can collect assessment data to monitor and document children's progress toward meeting Grade-Level Goals.

Lesson	Content Assessed	Where to Find It
12◆1	**Describe the relationship between days in one week and hours in one day.** [Measurement and Reference Frames Goal 3]	*TLG*, p. 867
12◆2	**Record addition and subtraction facts.** [Operations and Computation Goal 1]	*TLG*, p. 875
12◆3	**Identify units of time.** [Measurement and Reference Frames Goal 3]	*TLG*, p. 879
12◆4	**Solve problems involving multiplication.** [Operations and Computation Goal 4]	*TLG*, p. 885
12◆5	**Use arrays to model multiplication facts.** [Operations and Computation Goal 4]	*TLG*, p. 891
12◆6	**Read a bar graph.** [Data and Chance Goal 2]	*TLG*, p. 897
12◆7	**Find landmarks of a data set.** [Data and Chance Goal 2]	*TLG*, p. 905

Math Boxes

Math Boxes, one of several types of tasks highlighted in the Recognizing Student Achievement notes, have an additional useful feature. Math Boxes in most lessons are paired or linked with Math Boxes in one or two other lessons that have similar problems. Paired or linked Math Boxes in Unit 12: 12-1 and 12-3; 12-2, 12-4, and 12-6; and 12-5, 12-7, and 12-8.

Writing/Reasoning Prompts

In Unit 12, a variety of writing prompts encourage children to explain their strategies and thinking, to reflect on their learning, and to make connections to other mathematics or life experiences. Here are some of the Unit 12 suggestions:

Lesson	Writing/Reasoning Prompts	Where to Find It
12♦1	Explain how you found the correct amount of change.	*TLG*, p. 869
12♦4	Explain how you found the solution to a problem involving money.	*TLG*, p. 885
12♦5	Explain how you found the missing numbers in ___ − 23 = 17 and 60 − ___ = 28.	*TLG*, p. 894

Portfolio Opportunities

Portfolios are a versatile tool for assessment. They help children reflect on their mathematical growth and help teachers understand and document that growth. Each unit identifies several student products that can be selected and stored in a portfolio. Here are some of the Unit 12 suggestions:

Lesson	Portfolio Opportunities	Where to Find It
12♦1	Children explain how to find change in a money problem.	*TLG*, p. 869
12♦3	Children answer problems involving units of time.	*TLG*, p. 879
12♦4	Children solve multiplication problems using counters and drawings.	*TLG*, p. 885
12♦4	Children explain their solutions to problems involving equal groups and money.	*TLG*, p. 888
12♦5	Children explain how to find the missing numbers in a number sentence involving subtraction.	*TLG*, p. 894

Periodic Assessment

Every Progress Check lesson includes opportunities to observe children's progress and to collect student products in a variety of ways—Self Assessment, Oral and Slate Assessment, Written Assessment, and an Open Response task. For more details, see the first page of Progress Check 12, Lesson 12-8, page 908, of the *Teacher's Lesson Guide*.

Progress Check Modifications

Written Assessments are one way children demonstrate what they know. The table below shows modifications for the Written Assessment in this unit. Use these to maximize opportunities for children to demonstrate what they know. Modifications can be given individually or written on the board for the class.

Problem(s)	Modifications for Written Assessment
1–6	For Problems 1–6, write each person's name and the number of miles they ran on a separate stick-on note, and organize the stick-on notes from least to greatest miles.
8–11	For Problems 8–11, use page 86 in *My Reference Book* to solve the problems.
13	For Problem 13, explain how you put the numbers in order.
15–20	For Problems 15–20, draw arrays to solve the problems.

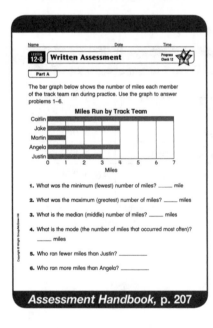

Assessment Handbook, p. 207

The Written Assessment for the Unit 12 Progress Check is on pages 207–209.

Open Response, *Getting to School*

Description

For this task, children analyze a bar graph and answer and write questions based on the information in the graph.

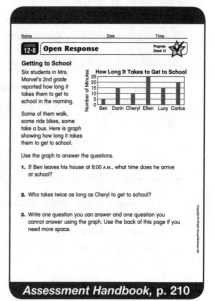

Assessment Handbook, p. 210

Focus

◆ **Use graphs to ask, answer simple questions, and draw conclusions.**
[Data and Chance Goal 2]

◆ **Use mental arithmetic, paper, and pencil to solve problems involving the addition and subtraction of whole numbers.**
[Operations and Computation Goal 2]

Implementation Tips

◆ Review the labels on the bar graph, and discuss the intervals for the number of minutes.

◆ Clarify that both questions the children write for Problem 3 should relate to the information shown in the graph.

Modifications for Meeting Diverse Needs

◆ Enlarge the graph, and have children label each bar with its total number of minutes before answering the questions.

◆ Present the following two questions, and have children explain why they cannot use the graph to answer the questions.

1. *Who walks faster, Lucy or Carlos?*

2. *Does Darin get to school before Ellen?*

Improving Open Response Skills

Before children begin the task, display a copy of the graph on the overhead projector. Have children discuss in small groups what they know and what they do not know from the graph. For example, *I know it takes Ellen the longest to get to school; I do not know who starts out the earliest.* Have small groups report some of their thoughts about the graph. Distribute the task, and have children explain why it helps to think about the graph before reading the problems.

Note: The wording and formatting of the text on the student samples that follow may vary slightly from the actual task your children will complete. These minor discrepancies will not affect the implementation of the task.

Rubric

This rubric is designed to help you assess levels of mathematical performance on this task. It emphasizes mathematical understanding with only a mention of clarity of explanation. Consider the expectations of standardized tests in your area when applying a rubric. Modify this sample rubric as appropriate.

4	Answers the questions correctly. Writes one question that clearly cannot be answered, and another that can be answered, based on the information in the graph.
3	Answers the questions correctly. Writes two questions. One or both questions can be answered based on the information in the graph. Might write a question related to the context of the graph that cannot be answered, but this question might not be based directly on the information in the graph.
2	Answers the questions correctly. Writes two questions. The questions might relate to the context of the graph but not to the information in the graph. There might be some incorrect interpretations of the information in the graph.
1	Attempts to answer the questions, but one or both answers might be incorrect. Attempts to write two questions, but these questions might not relate to the context of the graph.
0	Does not attempt to solve the problem.

This Level 4 paper illustrates the following features: Problems 1 and 2 are correct. For Problem 3, the first question relates directly to the graph, but the answer cannot be derived from the information on the graph because it does not explain when Ellen leaves the house. The second question can be answered from the information on the graph.

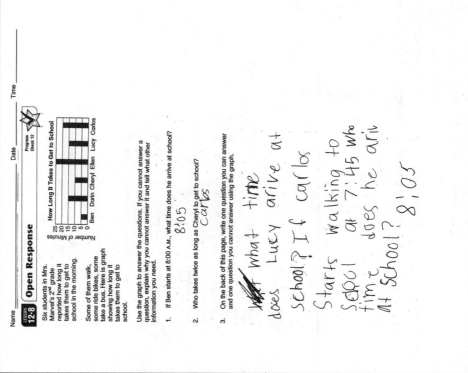

Name _____ Date _____ Time _____

LESSON 12·8 **Open Response** Progress Check 12

Six students in Mrs. Marvel's 2nd grade reported how long it takes them to get to school in the morning.

Some of them walk, some ride bikes, some take a bus. Here is graph showing how long it takes them to get to school.

How Long It Takes to Get to School

Number of Minutes: 25 20 15 10 5 0
Ben Dorin Cheryl Ellen Lucy Carlos

Use the graph to answer the questions. If you cannot answer a question, explain why you cannot answer it and tell what other information you need.

1. If Ben starts at 8:00 A.M., what time does he arrive at school? 8:05

2. Who takes twice as long as Cheryl to get to school? Carlos

3. On the back of this page, write one question you can answer and one question you cannot answer using the graph.

if Elen wkos up a 6:45
onda thither 15 minct to eat
bratfist. what tiem dose Elen get
to scholl?

II takes Ben 5 minct
to get to How take 5 tive min
as Ben?

This Level 4 paper illustrates the following features: Problems 1 and 2 are correct. For Problem 3, the first question cannot be answered because it does not tell what time Lucy leaves the house. The second question does specify when Carlos leaves, and the answer can be derived from the information on the graph.

Name _____ Date _____ Time _____

LESSON 12·8 **Open Response** Progress Check 12

Six students in Mrs. Marvel's 2nd grade reported how long it takes them to get to school in the morning.

Some of them walk, some ride bikes, some take a bus. Here is graph showing how long it takes them to get to school.

How Long It Takes to Get to School

Number of Minutes: 25 20 15 10 5 0
Ben Dorin Cheryl Ellen Lucy Carlos

Use the graph to answer the questions. If you cannot answer a question, explain why you cannot answer it and tell what other information you need.

1. If Ben starts at 8:00 A.M., what time does he arrive at school? 8:05

2. Who takes twice as long as Cheryl to get to school? Carlos

3. On the back of this page, write one question you can answer and one question you cannot answer using the graph.

What what time does Lucy arive at school? If carlos starts walking to soool at 7:45 Who time does he ariv At school? 8:05

This Level 3 paper illustrates the following features: Problems 1 and 2 are correct. For Problem 3, both questions relate to the graph. The first question can be answered. More clarification is needed to indicate what the second question is asking. It can be answered in terms of travel time, but it cannot be answered in terms of method of travel.

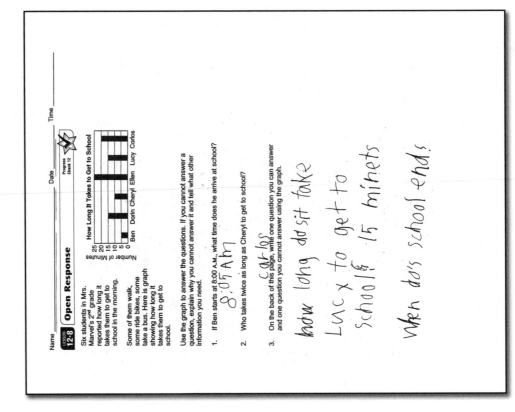

This Level 3 paper illustrates the following features: Problems 1 and 2 are correct. For Problem 3, the first question can be answered from the information in the graph. Although the second question has to do with school, it does not relate to the information provided, so this question cannot be answered from the information in the graph.

This Level 1 paper illustrates the following features: Problem 1 is correct. Problem 2 is incorrect. For Problem 3, the first question includes an answer, but the question cannot be answered from the information on the graph. The second question is not related to the information provided.

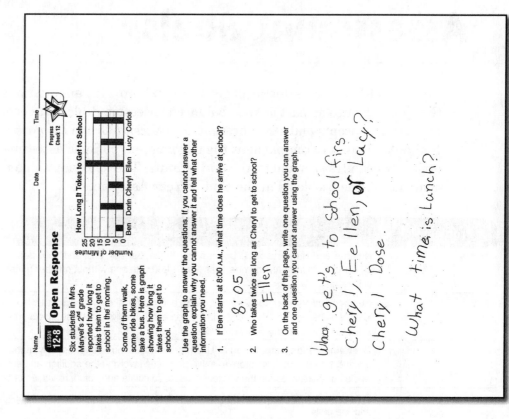

This Level 2 paper illustrates the following features: Problems 1 and 2 are correct. For Problem 3, both questions relate to the context of the graph, but neither question can be answered from the graph.

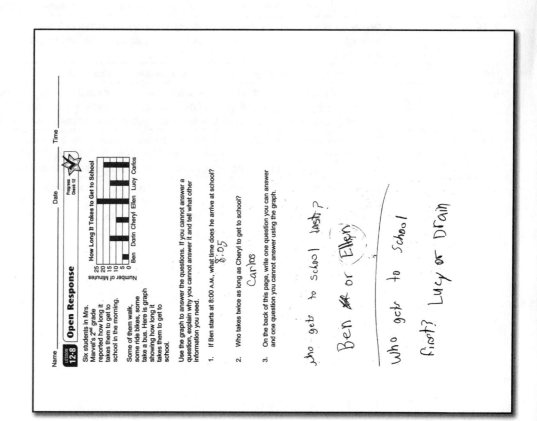

End-of-Year Assessment Goals

The End-of-Year Assessment (pages 227–232) provides an additional opportunity that you may use as part of your balanced assessment plan. It covers some of the important concepts and skills presented in *Second Grade Everyday Mathematics*. It should be used to complement the ongoing and periodic assessments that appear within lessons and at the end of units. The following table provides the goals for all the problems in the End-of-Year Assessment.

Problem(s)	Grade-Level Goal
1	**Number and Numeration 1:** Count on by 1s, 2s, 5s, 10s, 25s, and 100s past 1,000 and back by 1s, 10s, and 100s from any number less than 1,000 with and without number grids, number lines, and calculators.
2	**Number and Numeration 2:** Read, write, and model with manipulatives whole numbers up to 10,000; identify places in such numbers and the values of the digits in those places; read and write money amounts in dollars-and-cents notation.
3	**Operations and Computation 2:** Use manipulatives, number grids, tally marks, mental arithmetic, paper & pencil, and calculators to solve problems involving the addition and subtraction of multidigit whole numbers; describe the strategies used; calculate and compare values of coin and bill combinations.
4a	**Data and Chance 1:** Collect and organize data or use given data to create tally charts, tables, graphs, and line plots.
4b, 4c	**Data and Chance 2:** Use graphs to ask and answer simple questions and draw conclusions; find the maximum, minimum, mode, and median of a data set.
5, 6	**Measurement and Reference Frames 1:** Estimate length with and without tools; measure length to the nearest inch and centimeter; use standard and nonstandard tools to measure and estimate weight.
7, 8a	**Geometry 2:** Identify, describe, and model plane and solid figures including circles, triangles, squares, rectangles, hexagons, trapezoids, rhombuses, spheres, cylinders, rectangular prisms, pyramids, cones, and cubes.
8b	**Geometry 1:** Draw line segments and identify parallel line segments.
9	**Patterns, Functions, and Algebra 1:** Extend, describe, and create numeric, visual, and concrete patterns; describe rules for patterns and use them to solve problems; use words and symbols to describe and write rules for functions involving addition and subtraction and use those rules to solve problems.
10a	**Operations and Computation 2:** Use manipulatives, number grids, tally marks, mental arithmetic, paper & pencil, and calculators to solve problems involving the addition and subtraction of multidigit whole numbers; describe the strategies used; calculate and compare values of coin and bill combinations.
10b	**Patterns, Functions, and Algebra 2:** Read, write, and explain expressions and number sentences using the symbols $+$, $-$, $=$, $>$, and $<$; solve number sentences involving addition and subtraction; write expressions and number sentences to model number stories.

Problem(s)	Grade-Level Goal *continued*
11	**Operations and Computation 4:** Identify and describe change, comparison, and parts-and-total situations; use repeated addition, arrays, and skip counting to model multiplication; use equal sharing and equal grouping to model division.
12	**Number and Numeration 2:** Read, write, and model with manipulatives whole numbers up to 10,000; identify places in such numbers and the values of the digits in those places; read and write money amounts in dollars-and-cents notation.
13	**Operations and Computation 3:** Make reasonable estimates for whole number addition and subtraction problems; explain how the estimates were obtained.
14	**Data and Chance 3:** Describe events using *certain, likely, unlikely, impossible,* and other basic probability terms; explain the choice of language.
15	**Measurement and Reference Frames 2:** Partition rectangles into unit squares and count unit squares to find areas.
16	**Patterns, Functions, and Algebra 2:** Read, write, and explain expressions and number sentences using the symbols $+$, $-$, $=$, $>$, and $<$; solve number sentences involving addition and subtraction; write expressions and number sentences to model number stories.
17	**Number and Numeration 3:** Use manipulatives and drawings to model fractions as equal parts of a region or a collection; describe the models and name the fractions.
18	**Measurement and Reference Frames 3:** Describe relationships between days in a week and hours in a day.
19	**Number and Numeration 6:** Use manipulatives and drawings to model equivalent names for $\frac{1}{2}$.
20	**Measurement and Reference Frames 6:** Tell and show time to the nearest five minutes on an analog clock; tell and write time in digital notation.
21	**Number and Numeration 5:** Use tally marks, arrays, and numerical expressions involving addition and subtraction to give equivalent names for whole numbers.
22, 23	**Number and Numeration 7:** Compare and order whole numbers up to 10,000; use area models to compare fractions.
24	**Geometry 3:** Create and complete two-dimensional symmetric shapes or designs.
25, 26	**Operations and Computation 4:** Identify and describe change, comparison, and parts-and-total situations; use repeated addition, arrays, and skip counting to model multiplication; use equal sharing and equal grouping to model division.
27	**Patterns, Functions, and Algebra 3:** Describe the Commutative and Associative Properties of Addition and the Additive Identity and apply them to mental arithmetic problems.

Assessment Masters

Contents

LESSON 1·13 | Self Assessment

Check one box for each skill.

Skills	I can do this by myself. I can explain how to do this.	I can do this by myself.	I can do this with help.
1. Draw tally marks.			
2. Count money.			
3. Solve number-grid puzzles.			
4. Tell and write time.			
5. Add numbers to 10.			
6. Find missing numbers on a number line.			

LESSON 1·13 Written Assessment

Part A

1. Show 12 with tally marks. _____

2. Write the amount.

Total: _____

3. Fill in the missing numbers.

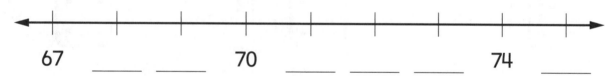

67 ____ ____ 70 ____ ____ ____ 74 ____

4. Write 3 names for 10.

_____

_____

_____

5. Write the time.   Draw hands to show 7:30.

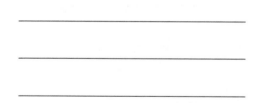   

____ : ____

LESSON 1·13 | **Written Assessment** *continued*

6. Fill in the missing numbers.

23		

		86

Part B

Find each missing number.

7.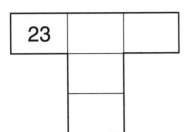
$$\begin{array}{r} 4 \\ + 6 \\ \hline \square \end{array}$$

8.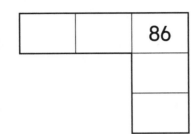
$$\begin{array}{r} 7 \\ + \square \\ \hline 12 \end{array}$$

9.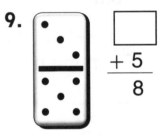
$$\begin{array}{r} \square \\ + 5 \\ \hline 8 \end{array}$$

10. Show four ways to make 25¢ using Ⓠ, Ⓓ, Ⓝ, and Ⓟ.

_____   _____

_____   _____

11. Write the number that is 10 less and 10 more.

Less		More
_____	75	_____
_____	90	_____
_____	106	_____
_____	137	_____

LESSON 1·13 | **Open Response**

The Missing Locker Numbers

Julie went to the museum with her mother. The museum has lockers to lock up coats and bags so you do not have to carry them. Once the lockers all had numbers, but now some of the numbers have rubbed off. This is what the lockers look like.

1	2	3	4	5
10		12	13	14
				23
28	29			32
		39		41

Fill in the numbers for all the lockers.

Julie wants to put her coat in the shaded locker in the middle. She says this locker is locker number 21. Is she right? Explain.

_____

_____

_____

_____

Color and describe at least one of the patterns you see in the locker numbers.

_____

_____

_____

LESSON 2·14 | Self Assessment

Check one box for each skill.

Skills	I can do this by myself. I can explain how to do this.	I can do this by myself.	I can do this with help.
1. Write fact families.			
2. Fill in name-collection boxes.			
3. Solve Frames-and-Arrows problems.			
4. Solve "What's My Rule?" problems.			
5. Know addition facts.			
6. Know subtraction facts.			

LESSON 2·14 **Written Assessment**

Part A

1. Add and write the turnaround.

    5 + 3 = _____   Turnaround _____

2. Write the fact family for 2, 11, and 9.

    _____   _____

    _____   _____

3. Add.

    a. 6 + 1 = _____

    b. 4 + 4 = _____

    c. 0 + 9 = _____

4. Subtract.

    a. 7 − 0 = _____

    b. _____ = 11 − 1

    c. 7 − 4 = _____

5. Fill in the empty frames.

Rule +5	20				40	

Written Assessment *continued*

Part B

6. Circle the names for 14.
Cross out names that do
not belong.

14

9 + 5   34 − 20   8 + 6

1 + 11   12 + 2   5 + 6

7 − 3   3 + 9

7 + 7   18 − 4

7. Find the rule and complete the table.

Rule

in	out
9	15
4	10
	12
7	
8	
10	16

8. Add.

  a.   9   **b.**   5
      + 6   + 6

9. Subtract.

  a.   9   **b.**   13
      − 5   − 8

LESSON 2·14 | **Written Assessment** *continued*

10. Put an X on the number in the tens place.

154   726

11. Show $1.00 two ways using 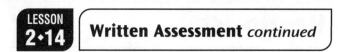.

12.

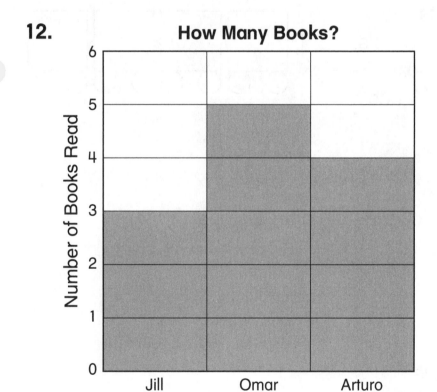

How Many Books?

Who read the most books? _____

Who read the fewest books? _____

How many books were read all together? _____

Open Response

Progress
Check 2

Train Boxes

In Flatland, trains make several stops a day. All the trains in Flatland have an engine. The engine picks up new boxes at each stop.

When the engine begins its day, it looks like this. It is 1 box long and it has 2 wheels.

At each stop, the train gets 3 more boxes and 6 more wheels. At the first stop, the train looks like this. It is 4 boxes long and it has 8 wheels.

1. Draw a picture of the Flatland train after 3 stops.

2. One train has 32 wheels.
   How many stops do you think it made?

Explain or show how you figured it out.

_____

_____

LESSON 3·9 | Self Assessment

Check one box for each skill.

Skills	I can do this by myself. I can explain how to do this.	I can do this by myself.	I can do this with help.
1. Add coins.			
2. Know addition facts.			
3. Count by 5s.			
4. Read a graph.			
5. Solve Frames and Arrows with 2 rules.			
6. Read the temperature.			

LESSON 3·9 | **Written Assessment** | Progress Check 3

Part A

1. You buy a green pepper for 27¢. Write Ⓟ, Ⓝ, Ⓓ, or Ⓠ to show the coins you could use to pay the exact amount.

2. Solve.

Unit

a. $\begin{array}{r} 7 \\ + 8 \\ \hline \end{array}$

b. $\begin{array}{r} 4 \\ + 6 \\ \hline \end{array}$

c. $9 + 5 =$ _____

d. $8 + 6 =$ _____

3. Count by 5s. Start at 0.

0, _____, _____, _____, _____, _____, _____, _____, _____, _____, _____

4. **How Many Pockets?**

a. Who has the most pockets? _____

b. Who has the fewest pockets? _____

LESSON 3·9 | **Written Assessment** *continued*

5. Jamal has 30 toy cars. Eric has 8 toy cars.
How many toy cars do Jamal and Eric have in all?

Answer: _____
(unit)

Part B

6. Fill in the frames.

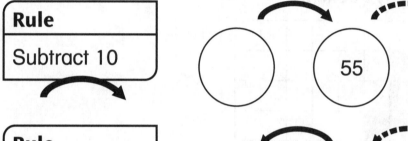

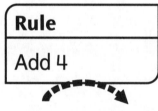

7. Solve.

a. _____ = 20 + 50

b. 30 + _____ = 70

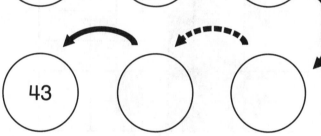

c.
$$
\begin{array}{r}
60 \\
+ \boxed{} \\
\hline
80
\end{array}
$$

d.
$$
\begin{array}{r}
70 \\
+ 50 \\
\hline
\end{array}
$$

Unit

8. Solve.

a.
$$
\begin{array}{r}
35 \\
+ 15 \\
\hline
\end{array}
$$

b.
$$
\begin{array}{r}
54 \\
- 12 \\
\hline
\end{array}
$$

Unit

LESSON 3·9 Written Assessment *continued*

9. You buy carrot juice for 60¢. You put 3 quarters in the vending machine.

How much change should you receive? _____

10. Count by 25s. Start at 0.

0, 25, 50, _____, _____, _____, _____, _____, _____

11.

How Many Pockets?

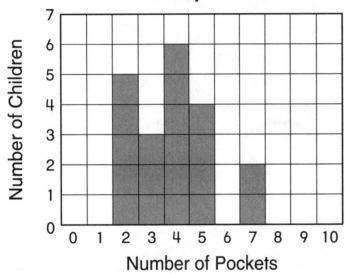

How many children have 5 pockets? _____

12. What is the temperature?

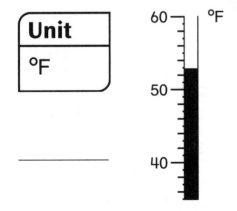

LESSON 3·9   Open Response

Buying from a Vending Machine

Carlos wants to buy chocolate
milk from the vending machine.
The milk costs 75 cents.
Carlos has 2 quarters,
5 dimes, and 5 nickels.

Show **all** the possible coin
combinations Carlos could
use to pay for the milk.
Use Ⓝ, Ⓓ, and Ⓠ to record your answers.

Explain how you know you found all the combinations.

_____

_____

_____

_____

LESSON 4·10 | **Self Assessment**   Progress Check 4

Check one box for each skill.

Skills	I can do this by myself. I can explain how to do this.	I can do this by myself.	I can do this with help.
1. Add coins.			
2. Solve 2-digit addition.			
3. Find change.			
4. Read the temperature.			
5. Find patterns on the number grid.			
6. Recognize odd and even numbers.			

LESSON 4·10

Written Assessment

Part A

1. How much?

Ⓠ, Ⓠ, Ⓓ, Ⓝ, Ⓟ

_____

2. Write the temperature shown on the thermometer.

a.

_____

b.
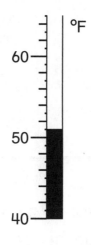

_____

3. **a.** 62 = _____ tens _____ ones

   b. 75 = _____ tens _____ ones

LESSON 4·10 | **Written Assessment** *continued*

4. Odd or even?

    a. 42 _____   **b.** 37 _____

    c. 101 _____   **d.** 564 _____

5. Fill in the grid.

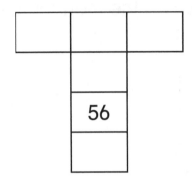

Part B

6. Luis bought an ice-cream cone for 37¢. He paid with 2 quarters. How much change did he get back?

_____

7. Becky brought 36 cupcakes to school for her birthday. She gave 10 away during lunch. How many cupcakes did she have then?

Answer: _____
        (unit)

Number model: _____

LESSON 4·10 **Written Assessment** *continued*

Make a ballpark estimate. Write a number model to show your estimate. Next, solve. Show your work.

8. Ballpark estimate:

a. _____

b.
```
   53
+ 66
```

9. Ballpark estimate:

a. _____

b.
```
   27
+ 48
```

10. Ballpark estimate:

a. _____

b.
```
   134
+ 137
```

Mark each thermometer to show the temperature.

11. 47°F

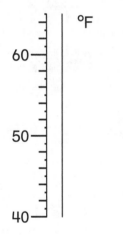

12. 63°F

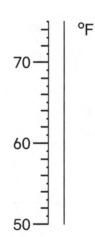

13. Circle the digit in the 100s place.

    a. 7,368   **b.** 10,431   **c.** 206

LESSON 4·10 | **Open Response**

Finding the Largest Sum

Cut out the 4 digits from the bottom of this page.

Make two 2-digit numbers in the boxes below so that when you add them you get the largest possible sum.

Use the digits you cut out to help you try different combinations. When you find the combination that makes the largest sum, write the numbers in the boxes.

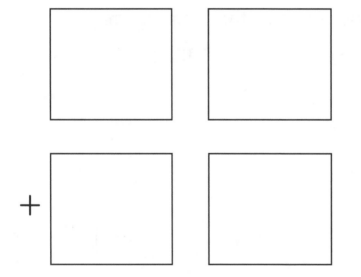

Show your work. Explain how you know you found the largest sum.

4   3   7   5

LESSON 5·9   Self Assessment

Check one box for each skill.

Skills	I can do this by myself. I can explain how to do this.	I can do this by myself.	I can do this with help.
1. Name polygons.			
2. Identify 3-D shapes.			
3. Find the lines of symmetry.			
4. Draw line segments.			
5. Count numbers in the thousands.			
6. Identify parallel lines.			

Part A

1. Write the fact family.

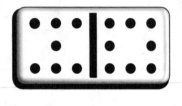

_____

_____

_____

_____

2. Fill in the counts.

1,294; 1,295; _____; _____; _____; _____;

_____; _____

3. Write the numbers in order from least to greatest.

849   674   1,647   647

_____

4. Draw line segments using your straightedge.

E   D
•   •

B   C
•   •

LESSON 5·9 | **Written Assessment** *continued*

In Problems 5–9, fill in the oval next to the correct answer.

5. This shape is a
- 0 hexagon.
- 0 rhombus.
- 0 square.

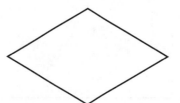

6. This shape is a
- 0 rectangle.
- 0 triangle.
- 0 trapezoid.

7. This is a picture of a
- 0 cube.
- 0 sphere.
- 0 pyramid.

Part B

8. This is a picture of a
- 0 cylinder.
- 0 cone.
- 0 sphere.

LESSON 5·9 **Written Assessment** *continued*

9. This is a picture of a

    O cylinder.

    O pyramid.

    O rectangular prism.

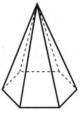

---

10. Draw line segment *AB*.

11. Draw a line segment that is parallel to line segment *AB*. Label its endpoints *C* and *D*.

12. Draw a line segment that is not parallel to line segment *AB*. Label its endpoints *E* and *F*.

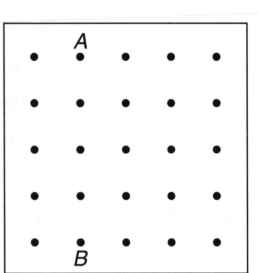

---

13. Find all the lines of symmetry for each shape.

 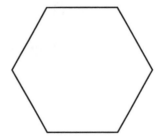

LESSON 5·9 | Open Response

Making Polygons

Jane put two pattern-block triangles together and traced around them to make a polygon.

This is what her polygon looked like.

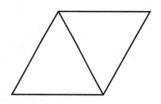

Make as many different polygons as you can, using 4 pattern-block triangles.

Use your Pattern-Block Template to record 3 of your polygons.

Use 4 pattern-block triangles to make a shape that is NOT a polygon. Use your Pattern-Block Template to record your shape.

Explain how you know your shape is NOT a polygon.

_____

_____

LESSON 6·11 | Self Assessment

Check one box for each skill.

Skills	I can do this by myself. I can explain how to do this.	I can do this by myself.	I can do this with help.
1. Tell time.			
2. Make a ballpark estimate.			
3. Solve "What's My Rule?" problems.			
4. Solve number stories.			
5. Compare numbers.			
6. Solve subtraction problems.			

LESSON 6·11 | **Written Assessment**

Progress Check 6

Part A

1. Write the time.

___:___

2. Fish K weighs 35 pounds. Fish G weighs 10 pounds. How much do they weigh together?

_____ pounds

Total	
Part	**Part**

3. Solve.

in	out
0	6
4	
14	
	12

Rule
_____

4. Write <, >, or =.

64 _____ 46

210 _____ 201

437 _____ 447

Part B

5. Make ballpark estimates. Write a number model for each estimate.

42 + 39

___ + ___ = ___

131 + 27

____ + ____ = ____

LESSON 6·11 | **Written Assessment** *continued*

6. Draw an array with 3 rows and 5 dots in each row.

How many dots in all? _____

Number model: _____

7. Fish J weighs 24 pounds. Fish H weighs 14 pounds. How much more does Fish J weigh?

_____ pounds more

Quantity
24

Quantity
14

_____
Difference

Solve.

8. 78	**9.** 64	**10.** 180
− 52	− 29	− 59

LESSON 6·11 | **Open Response**

Counting Cookies

There are a total of 52 cookies on 3 plates in my kitchen.

When I take away 14 cookies from the first plate, there are still 7 cookies left on the first plate.

There are 12 cookies on the second plate.

Write your own problem using the cookie information.

Solve your problem. Use counters or draw pictures.

Show your work and explain how you solved your problem.

LESSON 7·9 Self Assessment

Check one box for each skill.

Skills	I can do this by myself. I can explain how to do this.	I can do this by myself.	I can do this with help.
1. Solve number stories.			
2. Write number models.			
3. Make a bar graph.			
4. Double numbers.			
5. Name 3-D shapes.			

LESSON 7·9

Written Assessment

Part A

1. Marcus made 38 cupcakes for his birthday party.
   He gave out 20 cupcakes.

   a. How many cupcakes does Marcus have left?

   Answer: _____
   (units)

   b. Number model:

   _____

2. Use the data from the table to make a bar graph.

Heights of 2nd Graders

Height (in.)	Number
48	1
49	0
50	3
51	1
52	2
53	1
54	1

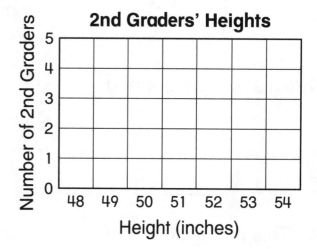

2nd Graders' Heights

LESSON 7·9 **Written Assessment** *continued*

3. Find the rule.

Rule

in	out
2	4
4	8
5	10
10	20
50	100

4. This is a picture of a

O   cube.

O   rectangular prism.

O   pyramid.

5. This is a picture of a

O   cube.

O   rectangular prism.

O   pyramid.

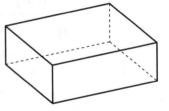

6. This is a picture of a

O   cube.

O   rectangular prism.

O   pyramid.

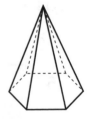

LESSON 7·9   **Written Assessment** *continued*

7. a. 9 + 11 + 8 = _____   **b.** 15 + 13 + 17 = _____

    c. 15 + 25 + 10 = _____   **d.** 12 + 8 + 6 + 4 = _____

Part B

8. Complete the table.

Rule
Halve

in	out
10	
20	
40	

9. Find the median (the middle number).

   a. 3, 4, 7 _____

   b. 3, 9, 7, 14, 12 _____

10. Find the median (the middle number) and the mode (the most popular number).

       27, 45, 63, 45, 50

median _____   mode _____

11. Fill in the missing numbers on the grid.

1,043		

LESSON 7·9 | **Open Response**

Dollars or Pennies?

Julie's aunt said she would pay Julie to do the dishes every day for one month.

She said she would pay Julie either $1.00 per week for 4 weeks, **or** 1 penny on the first day, 2 pennies on the second day, 4 pennies on the third day, doubling it every day for 30 days.

Which way should Julie get paid?

Draw, show, or explain how you solved the problem.

LESSON 8·8 | **Self Assessment**   Progress Check 8

Check one box for each skill.

Skills	I can do this by myself. I can explain how to do this.	I can do this by myself.	I can do this with help.
1. Read and write fractions.			
2. Think of things that are certain.			
3. Think of things that are impossible.			
4. Find lines of symmetry.			
5. Use pictures to compare fractions.			
6. Share things equally.			

LESSON 8·8

Written Assessment

Part A

1. Which shows $\frac{1}{4}$ shaded?
Fill in the oval.

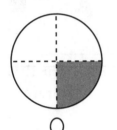
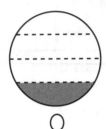

○   ○

Which fraction shows how much is shaded? Fill in the oval.

2.

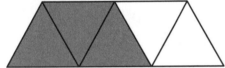

○   ○   ○
$\frac{3}{4}$ $\frac{3}{5}$ $\frac{3}{6}$

3.

○   ○   ○
$\frac{3}{4}$ $\frac{3}{6}$ $\frac{3}{8}$

---

4. Color $\frac{5}{8}$.

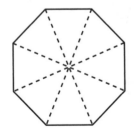

---

5. Color $\frac{1}{2}$.

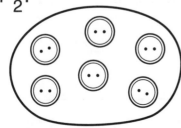

6. Color $\frac{7}{8}$.

LESSON 8·8 Written Assessment *continued*

7. Write one thing you are sure will happen today.

_____

8. Write one thing you are sure will not happen today.

_____

9. Which drawings have a line of symmetry?

○ 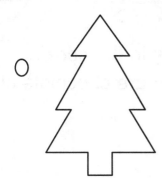 ○  ○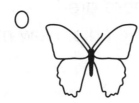

Part B

10. Color $\frac{1}{5}$.

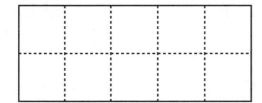

11. a. Divide into:

Halves   Fourths

Write <, >, or =.

b. $\frac{1}{2}$ _____ $\frac{1}{4}$ **c.** $\frac{2}{4}$ _____ $\frac{1}{2}$

LESSON 8·8 | **Written Assessment** *continued*

12. a. Three people share 6 pennies equally. How many pennies does each person

get? _____

b. $\frac{2}{3}$ of the pennies equals:

_____

13. Use counters to solve. There are 20 cookies in the cookie jar. $\frac{1}{4}$ of them are chocolate chip. How many are chocolate chip?

_____

LESSON 8·8 | Open Response

Sharing Brownies

Eric, Julia, Marcy, and Luiz wanted to share 3 big brownies so that they each had the same amount.

Eric said that it was not possible to share the 3 brownies equally. Julia said that it was easy and divided the brownies equally. What fraction did each person receive? Draw pictures to show your work. Explain your answer.

LESSON 9·10   Self Assessment

Check one box for each skill.

Skills	I can do this by myself. I can explain how to do this.	I can do this by myself.	I can do this with help.
1. Measure lines to the nearest inch and centimeter.			
2. Find area.			
3. Draw a line segment.			
4. Make a ballpark estimate.			
5. Find the median number.			
6. Add and subtract multidigit numbers.			

LESSON 9·10 | **Written Assessment**

Part A

Measure each line segment to the nearest inch and centimeter.

1. _____

_____ inches

_____ centimeters

2. _____

_____ inches

_____ centimeters

Find the area of each shape.

3.

Area = _____ sq cm

4.

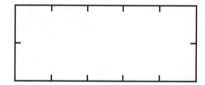

Area = _____ sq cm

5. Draw line segment *CD*.

```
C •   •   •   •   •

  •   •   •   •   •

  •   •   •   •   •

  •   •   •   •   •

  •   •   •   •  • D
```

LESSON 9·10 | **Written Assessment** *continued*

6. Make a ballpark estimate. Write a number model for the estimate.

37
+ 46

_____ + _____ = _____

7. 29, 30, 31, 32, 33

The median number of inches is _____.

Unit
inches

8. 8, 12, 7, 9, 11, 15, 10

The median number of meters is _____.

Unit
meters

Solve.

9. 23
+ 36

10. 134
+ 58

11. 86
− 41

12. 192
− 65

Part B

13. Measure the sides of the trapezoid to the nearest half-centimeter.

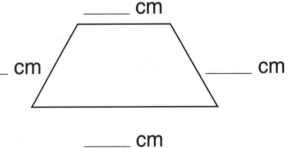

_____ cm

_____ cm   _____ cm

_____ cm

14. Write another name for $\frac{1}{2}$.

_____

15. Draw a line segment that is parallel to line segment *AB*. Label its endpoints *E* and *F*.

LESSON 9·10   **Open Response**   Progress Check 9

A Broken Ruler Problem

Victor is making a frame for his picture.

His picture is 10 inches high and 15 inches wide.

He decided to use popsicle sticks to make his frame.

Victor measured the length of a popsicle stick. His ruler is broken.

Here is a picture of what he did.

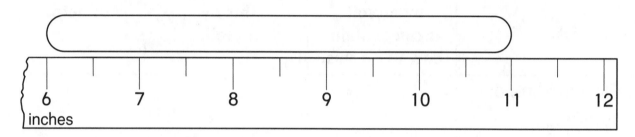

1. How many popsicle sticks will Victor need to make his frame?
   Show all your work.
   Draw and label pictures to show what you did.

2. Explain what you did to find your answer.

LESSON 10·12 | Self Assessment

Check one box for each skill.

Skills	I can do this by myself. I can explain how to do this.	I can do this by myself.	I can do this with help.
1. Find the line of symmetry.			
2. Read and write the temperature.			
3. Count by 1s in the 1,000s.			
4. Complete "What's My Rule?" tables.			
5. Estimate total cost.			
6. Add and subtract money amounts.			

LESSON 10·12 Written Assessment

Part A

1. Draw the lines of symmetry.

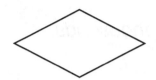

2. Count by 1s.

2,595, 2,596, _____, _____,

_____, _____, _____, _____

3. Mark the thermometer to show the temperature.

58°F

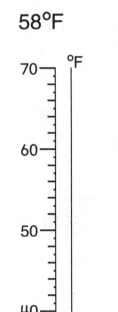

4. Write the temperature shown on the thermometer.

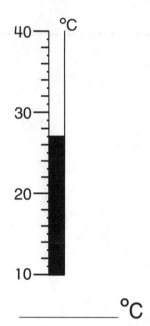

_____ °C

5. Find the rule and complete the "What's My Rule?" table.

in	out
150	200
325	375
400	
	550

Rule
_____

LESSON 10·12   **Written Assessment** *continued*

Use coins and bills. Write the amount.

6. $1 Ⓠ Ⓠ Ⓓ Ⓓ Ⓓ Ⓝ Ⓟ Ⓟ Ⓟ Ⓟ = $ _____

7. $1 Ⓠ Ⓠ Ⓠ Ⓠ Ⓠ Ⓓ Ⓓ Ⓝ Ⓝ Ⓝ Ⓟ Ⓟ Ⓟ = $ _____

Fill in the blanks. Write *ones, tens, hundreds,* or *thousands.*

8. The **3** in 3,051 stands for 3 _____.

9. The **8** in 1,938 stands for 8 _____.

10. The **2** in 9,245 stands for 2 _____.

Part B

11. You buy:

Oranges   and   Yogurt
1 lb at $1.49 lb   6-pack at $2.09

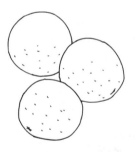   

a. Estimate the total cost.

Estimated cost: $ _____ + $ _____ = $ _____

b. Use a calculator. Find the exact cost. Write the amount in dollar-and-cents notation.

Exact cost: $ _____

Written Assessment *continued*

12. You buy a gallon of milk for $2.39. You give the cashier $5.00. How much change should you get? Show your work.

13. 3 people share 12 marbles. How many marbles does each person get?

_____ marbles

Show your work.

LESSON 10·12 | **Open Response**

Comparing Coins

Julian has 10 coins. Sue has 5 coins.

There is a total of 4 quarters.

Sue has more than $1.

Sue's coins are worth twice as much as Julian's coins.

Show Julian's 10 coins. Use Ⓟ, Ⓝ, Ⓓ, or Ⓠ.	How much money does Julian have?
Show Sue's 5 coins. Use Ⓟ, Ⓝ, Ⓓ, or Ⓠ.	How much money does Sue have?

Show your work. Explain how you found your answer.

_____

_____

_____

_____

_____

_____

_____

LESSON 11·10 | **Self Assessment**

Check one box for each skill.

Skills	I can do this by myself. I can explain how to do this.	I can do this by myself.	I can do this with help.
1. Make change.			
2. Share things equally.			
3. Draw arrays to solve problems.			
4. Compare fractions.			
5. Solve multidigit addition and subtraction problems.			

Written Assessment   Progress Check 11

Part A

1. Hector had $3.00. He spent $2.25.
   How much change should Hector get? _____

2. Tara had $5.00. She spent $3.60.
   How much change should Tara get? _____

3. Draw a picture or use counters to solve.
   16 pennies shared equally among 4 children.

   How many pennies does each child get? _____

Draw an array to solve each problem.

4. $3 \times 6 =$ _____

5. $5 \times 4 =$ _____

6. $8 \times 3 =$ _____

LESSON 11·10 | **Written Assessment** *continued*

Use your Fraction Cards to help.
Write <, >, or =.

> < means less than
> > means more than
> = means equal to

7. $\dfrac{1}{3}$ _____ $\dfrac{1}{2}$

8. $\dfrac{6}{8}$ _____ $\dfrac{1}{2}$

9. $\dfrac{2}{6}$ _____ $\dfrac{1}{2}$

10. $\dfrac{2}{3}$ _____ $\dfrac{4}{6}$

Solve. Show your work. Record your answer.

11. $\begin{array}{r} 23 \\ + 48 \\ \hline \end{array}$

12. $\begin{array}{r} 142 \\ +169 \\ \hline \end{array}$

13. $\begin{array}{r} 34 \\ - 18 \\ \hline \end{array}$

14. $\begin{array}{r} 168 \\ - 49 \\ \hline \end{array}$

Part B

Add or subtract. Use your tool-kit coins.

15. $\begin{array}{r} \$1.30 \\ - \$0.64 \\ \hline \end{array}$

16. $\begin{array}{r} \$3.46 \\ + \$1.78 \\ \hline \end{array}$

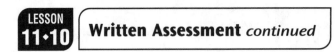

LESSON 11·10 | **Written Assessment** *continued*

For each number story, fill in a multiplication/division diagram.
Then use counters, arrays, or pictures to find the answer.

17. 5 baskets.

3 balls in each basket.

How many balls in all? _____

baskets	balls per basket	balls in all

Number model: _____

18. 2 boxes of crayons.

10 crayons in all.

How many crayons in each box? _____

boxes	crayons per box	crayons in all

Number model: _____

Open Response

LESSON 11·10

Sharing Candy

Kenji did not have enough pieces of candy to share equally with his 7 friends. He had 25 pieces of candy. How many more pieces does Kenji need so all 8 children will get an equal amount of candy?

_____

Explain how you found your answer in pictures **and** words. Write a number sentence you used to solve the problem.

LESSON 12·8 | **Self Assessment**

Check one box for each skill.

Skills	I can do this by myself. I can explain how to do this.	I can do this by myself.	I can do this with help.
1. Find the maximum and minimum of a data set.			
2. Find the median and mode of a data set.			
3. Make change.			
4. Find equivalent fractions for $\frac{1}{2}$.			
5. Order large numbers from smallest to largest.			

LESSON 12·8 | **Written Assessment** | Progress Check 12

Part A

The bar graph below shows the number of miles each member of the track team ran during practice. Use the graph to answer problems 1–6.

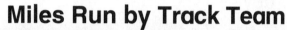

Miles Run by Track Team

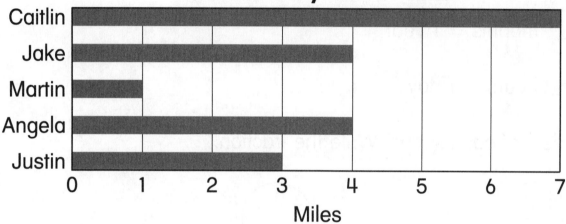

Miles

1. What was the minimum (fewest) number of miles? _____ mile

2. What was the maximum (greatest) number of miles? _____ miles

3. What is the median (middle) number of miles? _____ miles

4. What is the mode (the number of miles that occurred most often)? _____ miles

5. Who ran fewer miles than Justin? _____

6. Who ran more miles than Angela? _____

LESSON 12·8 **Written Assessment** *continued*

7. Use coins to help you. You have $1.00.
You spend $0.53. How much change do you get? _____

8. 1 hour = _____ minutes

9. 1 week = _____ days

10. _____ months = 1 year

11. _____ hours = 1 day

12. Shade $\frac{1}{2}$ of each shape. Write the fraction.

$\frac{1}{2}$ or _____ $\frac{1}{2}$ or _____

13. Write the numbers in order from smallest to largest.

9,246   9,642   9,426   9,462   9,624

_____ _____ _____ _____ _____
smallest   largest

LESSON
12·8 **Written Assessment** *continued*

Part B

14. Write the fact family for the Fact Triangle.

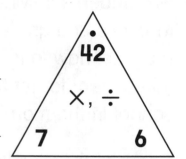

___ × ___ = ___   ___ ÷ ___ = ___

___ × ___ = ___   ___ ÷ ___ = ___

Solve.

15. 6 × 10 = _____   **16.** 2 × 7 = _____   **17.** _____ = 3 × 2

18. _____ = 4 × 5   **19.** _____ = 3 × 5   **20.** 7 × 10 = _____

Draw the hour and minute hands to match the time.

21.

4:12

22.

2:37

Open Response

Getting to School

Six students in Mrs. Marvel's 2nd grade reported how long it takes them to get to school in the morning.

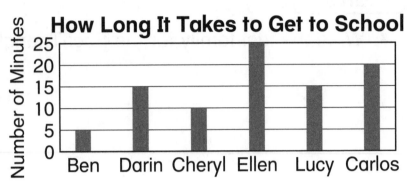

How Long It Takes to Get to School

Number of Minutes

Ben Darin Cheryl Ellen Lucy Carlos

Some of them walk, some ride bikes, some take a bus. Here is graph showing how long it takes them to get to school.

Use the graph to answer the questions.

1. If Ben leaves his house at 8:00 A.M., what time does he arrive at school?

2. Who takes twice as long as Cheryl to get to school?

3. Write one question you can answer and one question you cannot answer using the graph. Use the back of this page if you need more space.

LESSON 1·13 | **Written Assessment**   Progress Check 1

Part A

1. Show 12 with tally marks.   ~~HHT~~ ~~HHT~~ //

2. Write the amount.

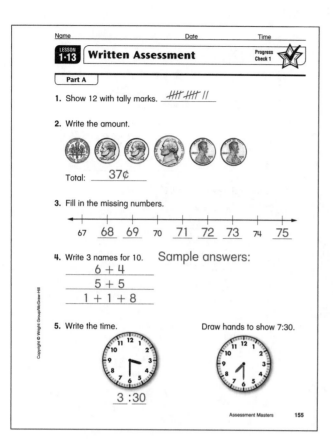

Total: _____37¢_____

3. Fill in the missing numbers.

67   **68**   **69**   70   **71**   **72**   **73**   74   **75**

4. Write 3 names for 10.   Sample answers:

_____6 + 4_____
_____5 + 5_____
_____1 + 1 + 8_____

5. Write the time.   Draw hands to show 7:30.

3 : 30

LESSON 1·13 | **Written Assessment** *continued*

6. Fill in the missing numbers.

23	**24**	25
	34	
	44	

84	85	86
	96	
	106	

Part B

Find each missing number.

7.   4   + 6   **10**

8.   7   + **5**   12

9.   **3**   + 5   8

10. Show four ways to make 25¢ using Ⓠ, Ⓓ, Ⓝ, and Ⓟ.

Sample answers: Ⓝ Ⓝ Ⓝ Ⓝ Ⓝ
Ⓓ Ⓓ Ⓝ   Ⓝ Ⓝ Ⓝ Ⓓ   Ⓓ Ⓓ Ⓟ Ⓟ Ⓟ Ⓟ Ⓟ

11. Write the number that is 10 less and 10 more.

Less		More
65	75	**85**
80	90	**100**
96	106	**116**
127	137	**147**

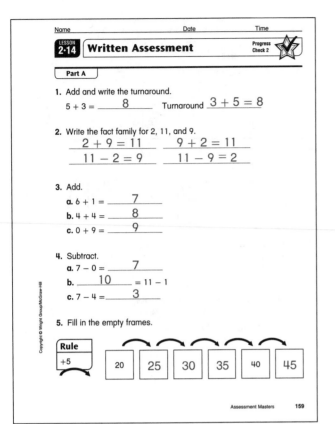

Name _____ Date _____ Time _____

LESSON 2·14 **Written Assessment**   Progress Check 2

Part A

1. Add and write the turnaround.

   5 + 3 = ___8___   Turnaround 3 + 5 = 8

2. Write the fact family for 2, 11, and 9.

   2 + 9 = 11   9 + 2 = 11
   11 − 2 = 9   11 − 9 = 2

3. Add.
   a. 6 + 1 = ___7___
   b. 4 + 4 = ___8___
   c. 0 + 9 = ___9___

4. Subtract.
   a. 7 − 0 = ___7___
   b. ___10___ = 11 − 1
   c. 7 − 4 = ___3___

5. Fill in the empty frames.

   Rule +5

   | 20 | 25 | 30 | 35 | 40 | 45 |

Name _____ Date _____ Time _____

LESSON 2·14 **Written Assessment** *continued*

Part B

6. Circle the names for 14. Cross out names that do not belong.

   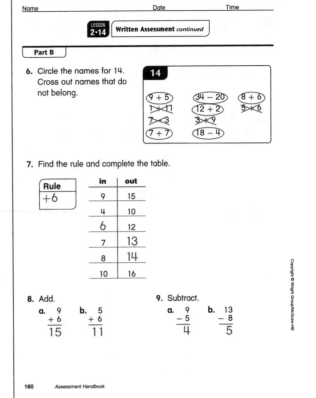

   14

   (9 + 5)   (34 − 20)   (8 + 6)
   ⋈11   (12 + 2)   ⋈6
   ⋈3   ⋈9
   (7 + 7)   (18 − 4)

7. Find the rule and complete the table.

   Rule +6

in	out
9	15
4	10
6	12
7	13
8	14
10	16

8. Add.
   a. 9
      + 6
      ———
      15
   b. 5
      + 6
      ———
      11

9. Subtract.
   a. 9
      − 5
      ———
      4
   b. 13
      − 8
      ———
      5

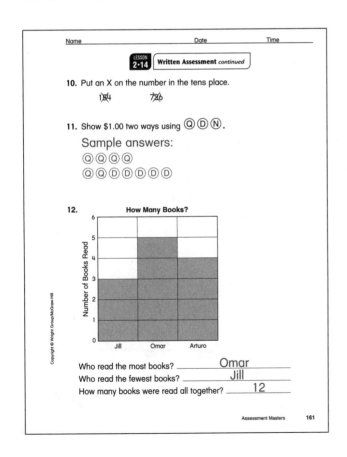

Name _____ Date _____ Time _____

LESSON 2·14 **Written Assessment** *continued*

10. Put an X on the number in the tens place.

    1⊠4   7⊠6

11. Show $1.00 two ways using Ⓠ Ⓓ Ⓝ.

    Sample answers:

    Ⓠ Ⓠ Ⓠ Ⓠ
    Ⓠ Ⓠ Ⓓ Ⓓ Ⓓ Ⓓ Ⓓ

12.

    How Many Books?

    Number of Books Read (y-axis, 0 to 6)

    Jill — 3
    Omar — 5
    Arturo — 4

    Who read the most books? ___Omar___
    Who read the fewest books? ___Jill___
    How many books were read all together? ___12___

Name _____ Date _____ Time _____

LESSON 3·9 | **Written Assessment** | Progress Check 3

Part A

1. You buy a green pepper for 27¢. Write Ⓟ, Ⓝ, Ⓓ, or Ⓠ to show the coins you could use to pay the exact amount.
   Sample answer: Ⓓ Ⓓ Ⓝ Ⓟ Ⓟ

2. Solve.

   a. 7   **b.** 4   **c.** $9 + 5 = \underline{14}$
       $+8$ $+6$
       $\overline{15}$ $\overline{10}$ **d.** $8 + 6 = \underline{14}$

Unit

3. Count by 5s. Start at 0.

   0, _5_, _10_, _15_, _20_, _25_, _30_, _35_, _40_, _45_, _50_

4.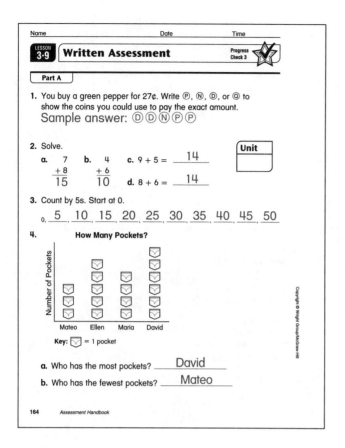
   How Many Pockets?

   Number of Pockets

   Mateo   Ellen   Maria   David

   Key: ▽ = 1 pocket

   a. Who has the most pockets? _____David_____

   b. Who has the fewest pockets? _____Mateo_____

Name _____ Date _____ Time _____

LESSON 3·9 | **Written Assessment** continued

5. Jamal has 30 toy cars. Eric has 8 toy cars.
   How many toy cars do Jamal and Eric have in all?
   Answer: _____38 toy cars_____
   (unit)

Part B

6. Fill in the frames.

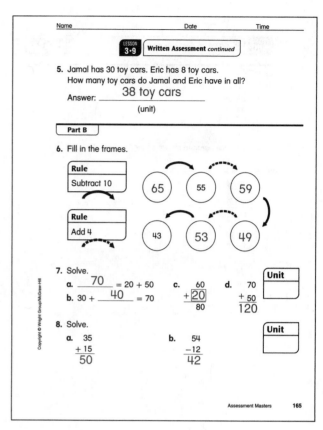

Rule
Subtract 10

   65   55   59

Rule
Add 4

   43   53   49

7. Solve.

   a. $\underline{70} = 20 + 50$ **c.**   60
   b. $30 + \underline{40} = 70$ $+20$
                                        $\overline{80}$

   d.   70
         $+50$
         $\overline{120}$

Unit

8. Solve.

   a.   35   **b.**   54
         $+15$ -12
         $\overline{50}$ $\overline{42}$

Unit

Name _____ Date _____ Time _____

LESSON 3·9 | **Written Assessment** continued

9. You buy carrot juice for 60¢. You put 3 quarters in the vending machine.

   How much change should you receive? _15¢_

10. Count by 25s. Start at 0.

    0, 25, 50, _75_, _100_, _125_, _150_, _175_, _200_

11.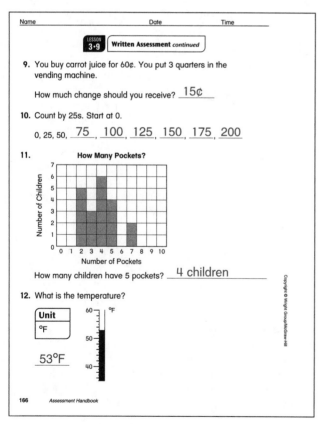
    How Many Pockets?

    Number of Children

    Number of Pockets

    How many children have 5 pockets? _4 children_

12. What is the temperature?

Unit
°F

    _53°F_

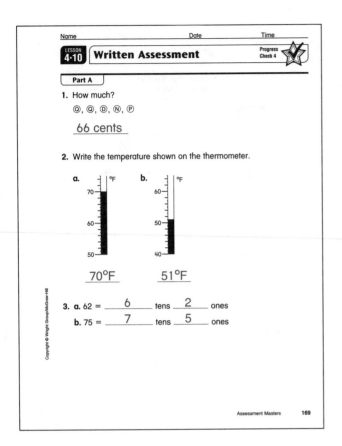

LESSON 4·10 **Written Assessment** Progress Check 4

Part A

1. How much?

   Q, Q, D, N, P

   __66 cents__

2. Write the temperature shown on the thermometer.

   a. °F
   70 —
   60 —
   50 —

   b. °F
   60 —
   50 —
   40 —

   __70°F__   __51°F__

3. **a.** 62 = ___6___ tens ___2___ ones
   b. 75 = ___7___ tens ___5___ ones

Copyright © Wright Group/McGraw-Hill

Assessment Masters   **169**

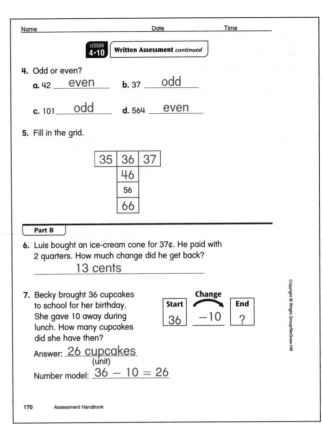

LESSON 4·10 **Written Assessment** *continued*

4. Odd or even?

   a. 42 __even__   **b.** 37 __odd__

   c. 101 __odd__   **d.** 564 __even__

5. Fill in the grid.

35	36	37
	46	
	56	
	66	

Part B

6. Luis bought an ice-cream cone for 37¢. He paid with 2 quarters. How much change did he get back?

   __13 cents__

7. Becky brought 36 cupcakes to school for her birthday. She gave 10 away during lunch. How many cupcakes did she have then?

Start	Change −10	End
36		?

   Answer: __26 cupcakes__
   (unit)

   Number model: __36 − 10 = 26__

Copyright © Wright Group/McGraw-Hill

170   *Assessment Handbook*

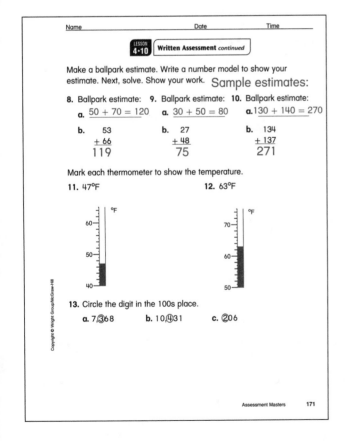

LESSON 4·10 **Written Assessment** *continued*

Make a ballpark estimate. Write a number model to show your estimate. Next, solve. Show your work.   Sample estimates:

8. Ballpark estimate:
   a. __50 + 70 = 120__

   b.   53
      + 66
      119

9. Ballpark estimate:
   a. __30 + 50 = 80__

   b.   27
      + 48
      75

10. Ballpark estimate:
   a. 130 + 140 = 270

   b.   134
      + 137
      271

Mark each thermometer to show the temperature.

11. 47°F

   °F
   60 —
   50 —
   40 —

12. 63°F

   °F
   70 —
   60 —
   50 —

13. Circle the digit in the 100s place.

   a. 7,368   **b.** 10,431   **c.** 206

Copyright © Wright Group/McGraw-Hill

Assessment Masters   **171**

LESSON 5·9 Written Assessment   Progress Check 5

Part A

1. Write the fact family.

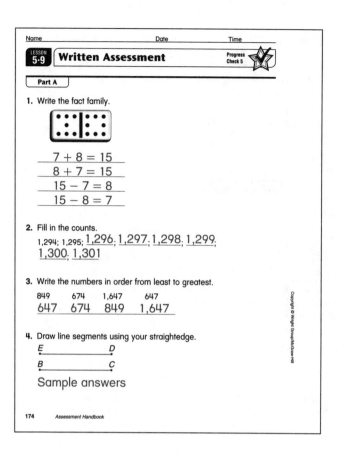

$$7 + 8 = 15$$
$$8 + 7 = 15$$
$$15 - 7 = 8$$
$$15 - 8 = 7$$

2. Fill in the counts.

1,294; 1,295; 1,296; 1,297; 1,298; 1,299; 1,300; 1,301

3. Write the numbers in order from least to greatest.

849   674   1,647   647

647   674   849   1,647

4. Draw line segments using your straightedge.

E   D

B   C

Sample answers

LESSON 5·9 Written Assessment *continued*

In Problems 5–9, fill in the oval next to the correct answer.

5. This shape is a
   - ○ hexagon.
   - ● rhombus.
   - ○ square.

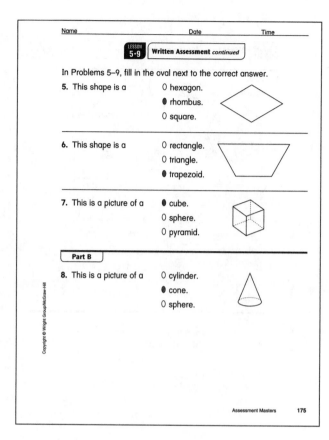

6. This shape is a
   - ○ rectangle.
   - ○ triangle.
   - ● trapezoid.

7. This is a picture of a
   - ● cube.
   - ○ sphere.
   - ○ pyramid.

Part B

8. This is a picture of a
   - ○ cylinder.
   - ● cone.
   - ○ sphere.

LESSON 5·9 Written Assessment *continued*

9. This is a picture of a
   - ○ cylinder.
   - ● pyramid.
   - ○ rectangular prism.

10. Draw line segment *AB*.

11. Draw a line segment that is parallel to line segment *AB*. Label its endpoints *C* and *D*.
    Sample answer

12. Draw a line segment that is not parallel to line segment *AB*. Label its endpoints *E* and *F*. Sample answer

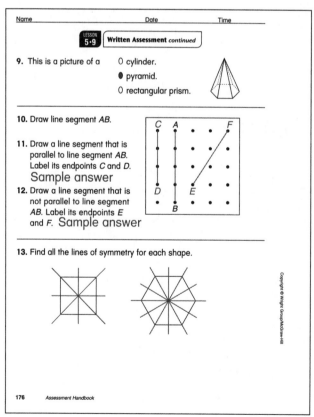

13. Find all the lines of symmetry for each shape.

LESSON 6·11 | **Written Assessment** | Progress Check 6

Part A

1. Write the time.

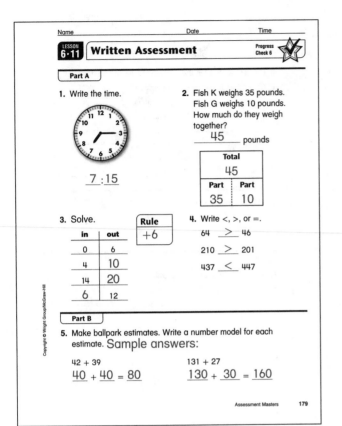

_7_ : _15_

2. Fish K weighs 35 pounds. Fish G weighs 10 pounds. How much do they weigh together?

_____45_____ pounds

Total
45

Part	Part
35	10

3. Solve.

Rule +6

in	out
0	6
4	10
14	20
6	12

4. Write <, >, or =.

64 _>_ 46

210 _>_ 201

437 _<_ 447

Part B

5. Make ballpark estimates. Write a number model for each estimate. Sample answers:

42 + 39
_40_ + _40_ = _80_

131 + 27
_130_ + _30_ = _160_

LESSON 6·11 | **Written Assessment** *continued*

6. Draw an array with 3 rows and 5 dots in each row.

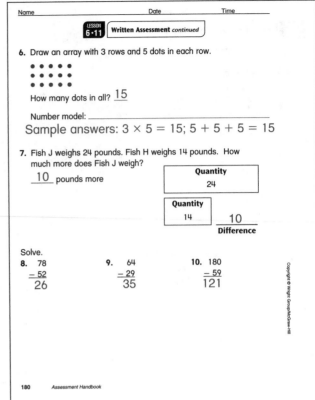

How many dots in all? _15_

Number model: _____
Sample answers: $3 \times 5 = 15$; $5 + 5 + 5 = 15$

7. Fish J weighs 24 pounds. Fish H weighs 14 pounds. How much more does Fish J weigh?

_10_ pounds more

Quantity
24

Quantity
14

_____10_____
Difference

Solve.

8. 78
− 52
—
26

9. 64
− 29
—
35

10. 180
− 59
—
121

LESSON 7·9 | **Written Assessment**

Progress Check 7

Part A

1. Marcus made 38 cupcakes for his birthday party. He gave out 20 cupcakes.

   a. How many cupcakes does Marcus have left?

      Answer: __18 cupcakes__
              (units)

   b. Number model: Sample answers:
      $38 - 20 = 18; 20 + 18 = 38$

2. Use the data from the table to make a bar graph.

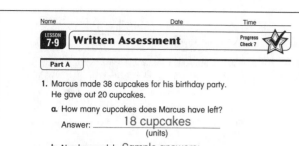

Heights of 2nd Graders

Height (in.)	Number
48	1
49	0
50	3
51	1
52	2
53	1
54	1

LESSON 7·9 | **Written Assessment** *continued*

3. Find the rule.

   Rule
   Double

in	out
2	4
4	8
5	10
10	20
50	100

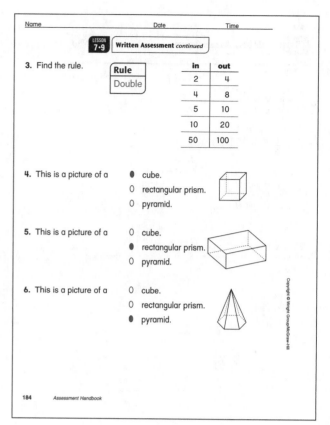

4. This is a picture of a
   ● cube.
   ○ rectangular prism.
   ○ pyramid.

5. This is a picture of a
   ○ cube.
   ● rectangular prism.
   ○ pyramid.

6. This is a picture of a
   ○ cube.
   ○ rectangular prism.
   ● pyramid.

LESSON 7·9 | **Written Assessment** *continued*

7. a. $9 + 11 + 8 =$ __28__   b. $15 + 13 + 17 =$ __45__
   c. $15 + 25 + 10 =$ __50__   d. $12 + 8 + 6 + 4 =$ __30__

Part B

8. Complete the table.

   Rule
   Halve

in	out
10	5
20	10
40	20

   Answers vary.

9. Find the median (the middle number).

   a. 3, 4, 7 __4__

   b. 3, 9, 7, 14, 12 __9__

10. Find the median (the middle number) and the mode (the most popular number).

    27, 45, 63, 45, 50

    median __45__   mode __45__

11. Fill in the missing numbers on the grid.

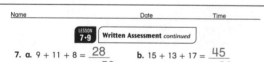

1,043	1,044	1,045
1,053		
1,063		

LESSON 8·8 **Written Assessment**   Progress Check 8

Part A

1. Which shows $\frac{1}{4}$ shaded?
   Fill in the oval.

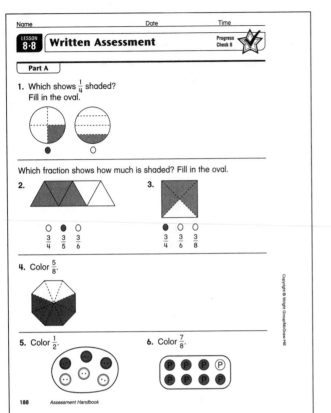

Which fraction shows how much is shaded? Fill in the oval.

2.   3.

○ ● ○   ● ○ ○
$\frac{3}{4}$ $\frac{3}{5}$ $\frac{3}{6}$ $\frac{3}{4}$ $\frac{3}{6}$ $\frac{3}{8}$

4. Color $\frac{5}{8}$.

5. Color $\frac{1}{2}$.   6. Color $\frac{7}{8}$.

LESSON 8·8 **Written Assessment** *continued*

7. Write one thing you are sure will happen today.
   <u>Sample answer: The sun will go down.</u>

8. Write one thing you are sure will not happen today.
   <u>Sample answer: An elephant will fly.</u>

9. Which drawings have a line of symmetry?

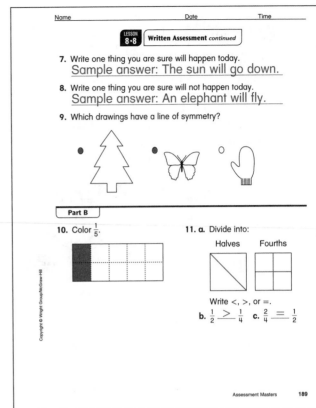

Part B

10. Color $\frac{1}{5}$.   11. **a.** Divide into:

                                        Halves   Fourths

                                        Write <, >, or =.
                                        b. $\frac{1}{2}$ __>__ $\frac{1}{4}$ **c.** $\frac{2}{4}$ __=__ $\frac{1}{2}$

LESSON 8·8 **Written Assessment** *continued*

12. **a.** Three people share 6
    pennies equally. How many
    pennies does each person
    get? <u>2 pennies</u>

    b. $\frac{2}{3}$ of the pennies equals:
    <u>4 pennies</u>

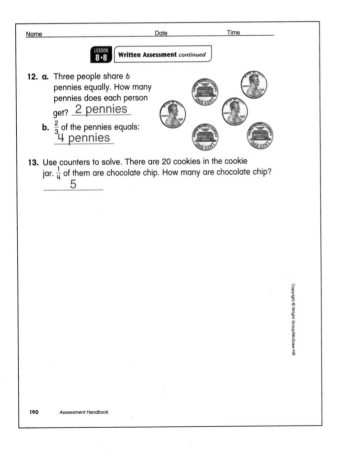

13. Use counters to solve. There are 20 cookies in the cookie
    jar. $\frac{1}{4}$ of them are chocolate chip. How many are chocolate chip?

    _____<u>5</u>_____

LESSON 9·10 Written Assessment

Progress Check 9

Part A

Measure each line segment to the nearest inch and centimeter.

1. _____

   __5__ inches

   __13__ centimeters

2. _____

   __3__ inches

   __8__ centimeters

Find the area of each shape.

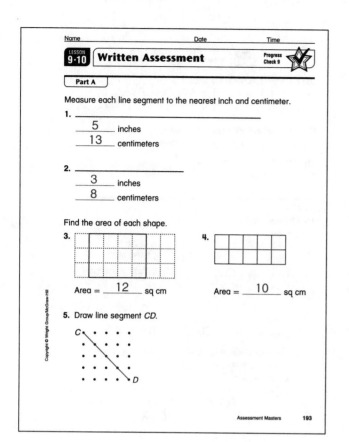

3. Area = __12__ sq cm

4. Area = __10__ sq cm

5. Draw line segment CD.

LESSON 9·10 Written Assessment *continued*

6. Make a ballpark estimate. Write a number model for the estimate. Sample answer:

   37
   + 46   __40__ + __50__ = __90__

7. 29, 30, 31, 32, 33

   The median number of inches is __31__.

   Unit: inches

8. 8, 12, 7, 9, 11, 15, 10

   The median number of meters is __10__.

   Unit: meters

Solve.

9. 23
   + 36
   __59__

10. 134
    + 58
   __192__

11. 86
   − 41
   __45__

12. 192
   − 65
   __127__

Part B

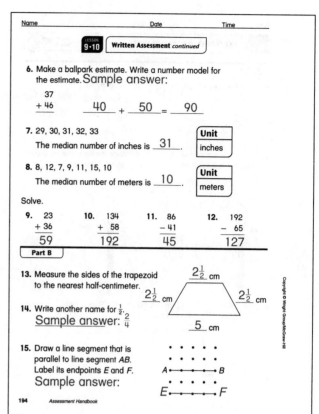

13. Measure the sides of the trapezoid to the nearest half-centimeter.

    $2\frac{1}{2}$ cm $2\frac{1}{2}$ cm $2\frac{1}{2}$ cm   __5__ cm

14. Write another name for $\frac{1}{2}$.

    Sample answer: $\frac{2}{4}$

15. Draw a line segment that is parallel to line segment AB. Label its endpoints E and F.

    Sample answer:

    A•——•——•——•B

    E•——•——•——•F

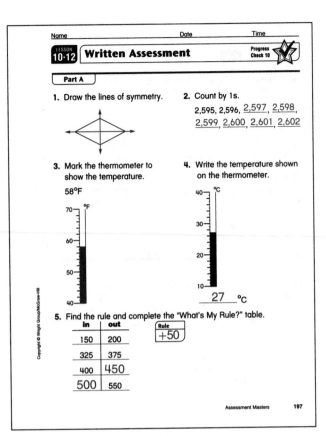

LESSON 10·12 **Written Assessment** Progress Check 10

Part A

1. Draw the lines of symmetry.

2. Count by 1s.

2,595, 2,596, _2,597_, _2,598_, _2,599_, _2,600_, _2,601_, _2,602_

3. Mark the thermometer to show the temperature.

58°F

4. Write the temperature shown on the thermometer.

_27_ °C

5. Find the rule and complete the "What's My Rule?" table.

in	out
150	200
325	375
400	450
500	550

Rule +50

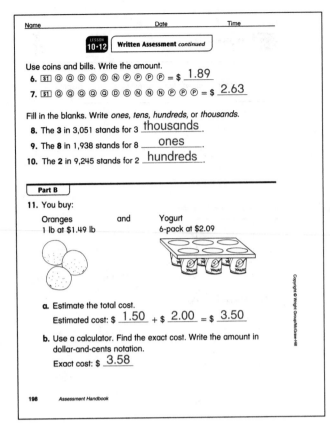

LESSON 10·12 **Written Assessment** *continued*

Use coins and bills. Write the amount.

6. $1 Ⓠ Ⓠ Ⓓ Ⓓ Ⓓ Ⓝ Ⓟ Ⓟ Ⓟ Ⓟ = $ _1.89_

7. $1 Ⓠ Ⓠ Ⓠ Ⓠ Ⓠ Ⓓ Ⓝ Ⓝ Ⓝ Ⓟ Ⓟ Ⓟ = $ _2.63_

Fill in the blanks. Write *ones, tens, hundreds,* or *thousands.*

8. The **3** in 3,051 stands for 3 _thousands_.

9. The **8** in 1,938 stands for 8 _ones_.

10. The **2** in 9,245 stands for 2 _hundreds_.

Part B

11. You buy:

Oranges   and   Yogurt
1 lb at $1.49 lb   6-pack at $2.09

a. Estimate the total cost.

Estimated cost: $ _1.50_ + $ _2.00_ = $ _3.50_

b. Use a calculator. Find the exact cost. Write the amount in dollar-and-cents notation.

Exact cost: $ _3.58_

LESSON 10·12 **Written Assessment** *continued*

12. You buy a gallon of milk for $2.39. You give the cashier $5.00. How much change should you get? Show your work.

$2.61 or about $2.60

13. 3 people share 12 marbles. How many marbles does each person get?

_4_ marbles

Show your work.

LESSON 11·10 Written Assessment

Progress Check 11

Part A

1. Hector had $3.00. He spent $2.25.
   How much change should Hector get? ___$0.75___

2. Tara had $5.00. She spent $3.60.
   How much change should Tara get? ___$1.40___

3. Draw a picture or use counters to solve.
   16 pennies shared equally among 4 children.
   How many pennies does each child get? ___4___

Draw an array to solve each problem.

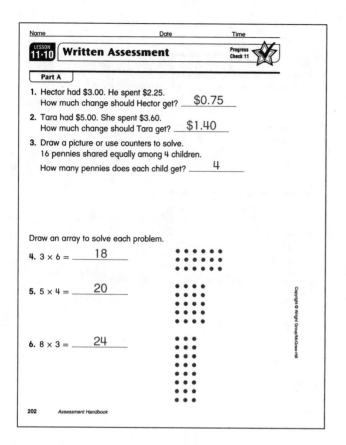

4. $3 \times 6 =$ ___18___

5. $5 \times 4 =$ ___20___

6. $8 \times 3 =$ ___24___

LESSON 11·10 Written Assessment continued

Use your Fraction Cards to help.
Write <, >, or =.

<	means less than
>	means more than
=	means equal to

7. $\frac{1}{3}$ ___<___ $\frac{1}{2}$

8. $\frac{6}{8}$ ___>___ $\frac{1}{2}$

9. $\frac{2}{6}$ ___<___ $\frac{1}{2}$

10. $\frac{2}{3}$ ___=___ $\frac{4}{6}$

Solve. Show your work. Record your answer.

11.
$$\begin{array}{r} 23 \\ + 48 \\ \hline 71 \end{array}$$

12.
$$\begin{array}{r} 142 \\ +169 \\ \hline 311 \end{array}$$

13.
$$\begin{array}{r} 34 \\ - 18 \\ \hline 16 \end{array}$$

14.
$$\begin{array}{r} 168 \\ - 49 \\ \hline 119 \end{array}$$

Part B

Add or subtract. Use your tool-kit coins.

15.
$$\begin{array}{r} \$1.30 \\ - \$0.64 \\ \hline \$0.66 \end{array}$$

16.
$$\begin{array}{r} \$3.46 \\ + \$1.78 \\ \hline \$5.24 \end{array}$$

LESSON 11·10 Written Assessment continued

For each number story, fill in a multiplication/division diagram.
Then use counters, arrays, or pictures to find the answer.

17. 5 baskets.
    3 balls in each basket.
    How many balls in all? ___15___

baskets	balls per basket	balls in all
5	3	?

Number model: ___$5 \times 3 = 15$___

18. 2 boxes of crayons.
    10 crayons in all.
    How many crayons in each box? ___5___

boxes	crayons per box	crayons in all
2	?	10

Number model: ___$10 \div 2 = 5$___

LESSON 12·8 | **Written Assessment** | Progress Check 12

Part A

The bar graph below shows the number of miles each member of the track team ran during practice. Use the graph to answer problems 1–6.

Miles Run by Track Team

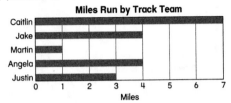

Miles

1. What was the minimum (fewest) number of miles? __1__ mile

2. What was the maximum (greatest) number of miles? __7__ miles

3. What is the median (middle) number of miles? __4__ miles

4. What is the mode (the number of miles that occurred most often)? __4__ miles

5. Who ran fewer miles than Justin? _Martin_

6. Who ran more miles than Angela? _Caitlin_

LESSON 12·8 | **Written Assessment** continued

7. Use coins to help you. You have $1.00. You spend $0.53. How much change do you get? _$0.47_

8. 1 hour = __60__ minutes

9. 1 week = __7__ days

10. __12__ months = 1 year

11. __24__ hours = 1 day

12. Shade $\frac{1}{2}$ of each shape. Write the fraction.

$\frac{1}{2}$ or $\frac{4}{8}$ $\frac{1}{2}$ or $\frac{3}{6}$

13. Write the numbers in order from smallest to largest.

9,246   9,642   9,426   9,462   9,624

_9,246_   _9,426_   _9,462_   _9,624_   _9,642_
smallest   largest

LESSON 12·8 | **Written Assessment** continued

Part B

14. Write the fact family for the Fact Triangle.

$7 \times 6 = 42$ $42 \div 6 = 7$

$6 \times 7 = 42$ $42 \div 7 = 6$

Solve.

15. $6 \times 10 = $ __60__   16. $2 \times 7 = $ __14__   17. __6__ $= 3 \times 2$

18. __20__ $= 4 \times 5$ 19. __15__ $= 3 \times 5$ 20. $7 \times 10 = $ __70__

Draw the hour and minute hands to match the time.

21.

4:12

22.

2:37

Beginning-of-Year Assessment

1. Write the numbers shown by the base-10 blocks.

a.

b.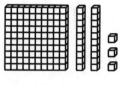

c.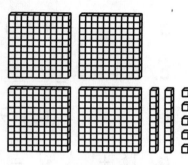

_____   _____

Draw a ◯ around the digit in the ones place.   _____

Draw a △ around the digit in the tens place.

2. a. Write at least three names for 10 in the box.

10

b. Circle the names in the box that **do not** belong.

12
̶H̶I̶T̶ ̶H̶I̶T̶ //
13 − 1   12 + 1
3 + 3 + 3 + 3
Ⓓ Ⓟ Ⓟ   12 − 0
6 + 6   Ⓠ
̶H̶I̶T̶ ̶H̶I̶T̶ /   11 + 0

Beginning-of-Year Assessment *continued*

3. Solve.

    a. _____ $= 4 + 0$ **b.** $7 + 1 =$ _____

    c. $6 + 4 =$ _____   **d.** $6 - 0 =$ _____

    e. _____ $= 18 - 9$ **f.** $7 + 7 =$ _____

    g. $16 +$ _____ $= 16$ **h.** $7 + 6 = 6 +$ _____

    i. $3 +$ _____ $= 3$ **j.** $8 +$ _____ $= 0 + 8$

4. Write the time.

    a.

        _____ : _____

    b.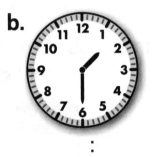

        _____ : _____

5. Fill in the empty frames.

Rule
+ 5

◯ (10) (15) ◯ (25)

Beginning-of-Year Assessment *continued*

6. Use the graph to answer the questions.

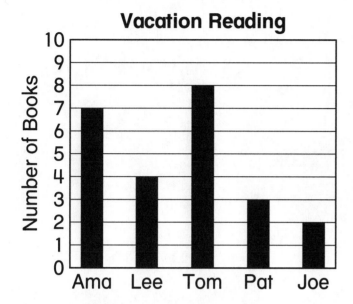

Vacation Reading

a. How many books did Lee read? _____

b. Who read the most books? _____

c. Who read the fewest books? _____

7. Jose's coins Ⓓ Ⓓ Ⓓ Ⓟ | Tameka's coins Ⓝ Ⓝ Ⓝ Ⓟ

Who has more money? _____

8. Circle the coins that are worth the same as one  .

LESSON 6·11 | **Mid-Year Assessment**

The temperature is

1.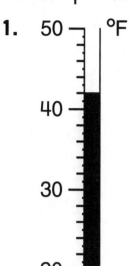

_____ °F.

2.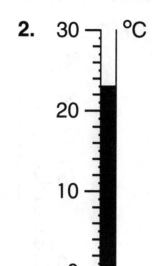

_____ °C.

Odd or Even?

3. 42 _____

4. 37 _____

5. 101 _____

6. 563 _____

7. Match.

LESSON 6·11 | **Mid-Year Assessment** *continued*

Shade each thermometer to show the temperature.

8. 57°F   **9.** 16°C

10. Show three ways to make 50¢.
Use Ⓠ, Ⓓ, Ⓝ, and Ⓟ.

11. **a.** Is the number 168 odd or even? _____

b. Explain how you know.

_____

_____

_____

LESSON 6·11 | **Mid-Year Assessment** *continued*

12. Sally's game mat for the *Money Exchange Game* looks like this:

One Dollar $1	Ten Cents 10¢	One Cent 1¢
	(dimes)	(pennies)

Draw $1, Ⓓ, Ⓟ on the blank game mat to show the exchanges she can make.

One Dollar $1	Ten Cents 10¢	One Cent 1¢

13. Justin's coins

Use Ⓓ, Ⓝ, and Ⓟ to show this amount with fewer coins.

Show the same amount using a different combination of coins.

LESSON 6·11 | **Mid-Year Assessment** *continued*

January						
Sun	Mon	Tue	Wed	Thu	Fri	Sat
		1	2	3	4	5
6	7	8	9	10	11	12
13	14	15	16	17	18	19
20	21	22	23	24	25	26
27	28	29	30	31		

14. There are _____ days in 1 week.

15. Circle the coin combinations that DO NOT belong.

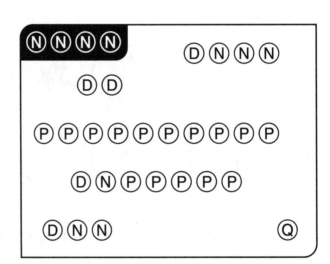

16. There are _____ minutes in 1 hour.

17. There are _____ hours in 1 day.

LESSON 12·8 | **End-of-Year Assessment**

1. Count by 10s. Start at 2,166.

2,166; _____; _____; _____; _____; _____

2. In 8,603,

the value of 6 is _____.

the value of 0 is _____.

the value of 8 is _____.

the value of 3 is _____.

3. Solve.

				Unit
a. 56 +67	**b.** 342 +139	**c.** 64 −39	**d.** 256 −178	fish

4. a. Complete the graph.
Tia read 6 books.
Ian read 3 books.
Theo read 5 books.
Jen read 3 books.

b. Median number of books

read: _____

c. Mode number of books

read: _____

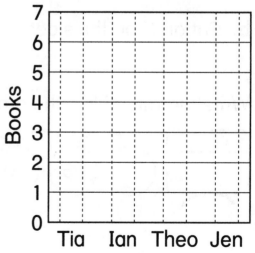

Number of Books Read

LESSON 12·8 **End-of-Year Assessment** *continued*

5. Measure this line segment to the nearest inch and to the nearest centimeter.

_____

_____ inches   _____ centimeters

6. Fill in the oval for the best answer. A second grader may weigh about

   ⬭ 60 pounds.   ⬭ 60 feet.

   ⬭ 60 ounces.   ⬭ 60 cups.

7. This is a picture of a

   ⬭ pyramid.

   ⬭ cylinder.

   ⬭ rectangular prism.

8. a. Write the name of the shape. Use the words in the box to help you.

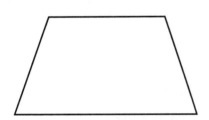

hexagon	rectangle
rhombus	trapezoid

_____

b. Put an X on the sides that are parallel.

9. Write the rule. Fill in the empty frames.

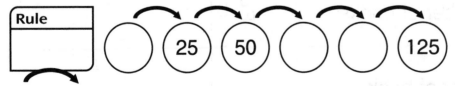

LESSON 12·8

End-of-Year Assessment *continued*

10. Use bills and coins to solve.

Ian saved $4.50 for his mother's birthday present.
His sister saved $3.40. How much money did they
save in all?

a. Answer: _____

b. Number model: _____

11. Draw an array to match the number story.

5 crayons in each box

2 boxes of crayons

12. Kali has 125 pennies. Write Kali's money amount in
dollars-and-cents notation. $_____._____

13. a. What do you think is a good estimate for 138 + 263?

_____

b. How did you get your estimate?

_____

_____

_____

**LESSON
12·8**

End-of-Year Assessment *continued*

14. Write a sentence about something that is likely to happen today.

_____

15. Use the tick marks to draw lines to show square units. Then count the squares to find the area.

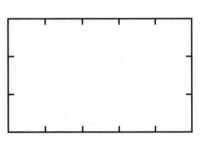

Area = _____ square cm

16. Use =, +, or −.

a. 8 ☐ 6 = 14   **b.** 15 ☐ 5 = 10

c. 25 ☐ 15 + 10   **d.** 18 = 10 ☐ 8

17. What fraction of the circles is shaded? _____

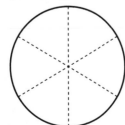

18. Complete.

a. 1 week = _____ days   **b.** _____ hours = 1 day

19. Shade $\frac{1}{2}$ and write the fraction.

$\frac{1}{2}$ or _____

20. Write the time.

a.

_____ : _____

b.

_____ : _____

21. Circle the names that DO NOT belong in the collection box.

25

$75 - 25$

$10 + 10$

$10 + 15$

$5 + 5 + 5 + 5$

$30 - 5$ $100 - 50$

22. a. Circle the largest number.

3,241   3,421   3,204   3,021

b. Write the numbers in order from smallest to largest.

_____; _____; _____; _____
  smallest   largest

LESSON 12·8 | **End-of-Year Assessment** *continued*

23. Circle the larger fraction.

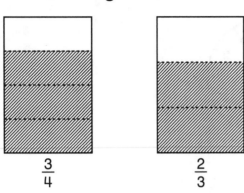

$\frac{3}{4}$ $\frac{2}{3}$

24. Draw two lines of symmetry.

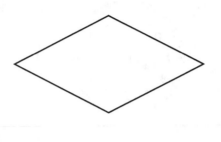

25. Fill in the diagram if needed.

Fish P weighs 36 pounds.
Fish M weighs 22 pounds.
How much more does Fish P weigh?

Fish P weighs _____ pounds more.

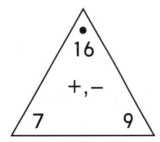

Quantity

Quantity

_____
Difference

26. Use counters or drawings to solve.

   a. 15 stickers, 3 children

      How many stickers per child? _____ stickers

   b. 40 candies, 4 candies per child

      How many children? _____ children

27. Write two addition facts for the fact triangle.

16

+,−

7   9

_____ + _____ = _____

_____ + _____ = _____

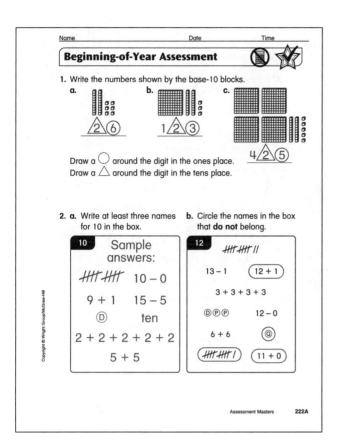

Beginning-of-Year Assessment

1. Write the numbers shown by the base-10 blocks.

a. 2̲6̲

b. 1̲2̲3̲

c. 4̲2̲5̲

Draw a ◯ around the digit in the ones place.
Draw a △ around the digit in the tens place.

2. a. Write at least three names for 10 in the box.

b. Circle the names in the box that **do not** belong.

10	Sample answers:
‖‖‖ ‖‖‖	10 − 0
9 + 1	15 − 5
Ⓓ	ten
2 + 2 + 2 + 2 + 2	
5 + 5	

12	‖‖‖ ‖‖‖ ‖‖
13 − 1	(12 + 1)
3 + 3 + 3 + 3	
Ⓓ Ⓟ Ⓟ	12 − 0
6 + 6	Ⓠ
(‖‖‖ ‖‖‖ ‖)	(11 + 0)

Assessment Masters   **222A**

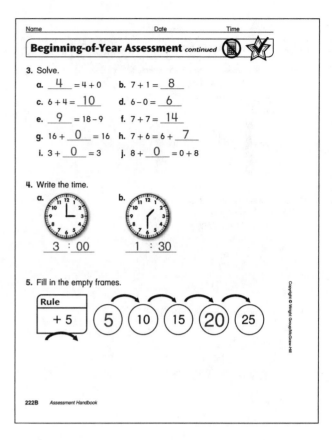

Beginning-of-Year Assessment *continued*

3. Solve.

a. 4̲ = 4 + 0   b. 7 + 1 = 8̲

c. 6 + 4 = 1̲0̲   d. 6 − 0 = 6̲

e. 9̲ = 18 − 9   f. 7 + 7 = 1̲4̲

g. 16 + 0̲ = 16   h. 7 + 6 = 6 + 7̲

i. 3 + 0̲ = 3   j. 8 + 0̲ = 0 + 8

4. Write the time.

a. 3 : 00

b. 1 : 30

5. Fill in the empty frames.

Rule: + 5

5 → 10 → 15 → 20 → 25

222B   Assessment Handbook

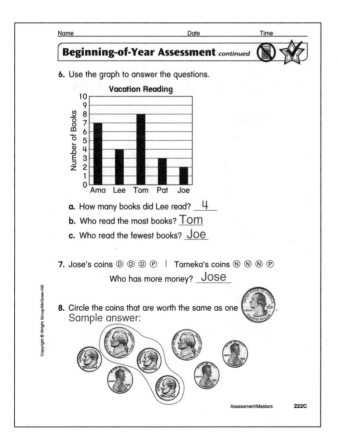

Beginning-of-Year Assessment *continued*

6. Use the graph to answer the questions.

Vacation Reading

(bar graph: Number of Books vs Ama, Lee, Tom, Pat, Joe)

a. How many books did Lee read? 4̲

b. Who read the most books? Tom

c. Who read the fewest books? Joe

7. Jose's coins Ⓓ Ⓓ Ⓓ Ⓟ | Tameka's coins Ⓝ Ⓝ Ⓝ Ⓟ

Who has more money? Jose

8. Circle the coins that are worth the same as one quarter.
Sample answer:

AssessmentMasters   **222C**

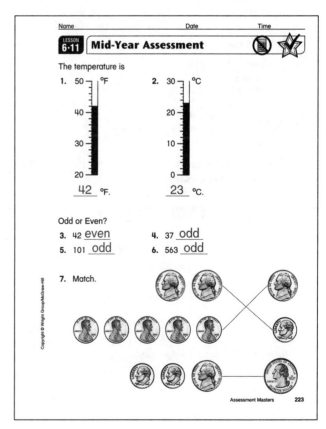

LESSON 6·11   **Mid-Year Assessment**

The temperature is

1. 42 °F.

2. 23 °C.

Odd or Even?

3. 42 even   4. 37 odd

5. 101 odd   6. 563 odd

7. Match.

Assessment Masters   **223**

Assessment Masters   **233**

LESSON 6·11 | **Mid-Year Assessment** *continued*

Shade each thermometer to show the temperature.

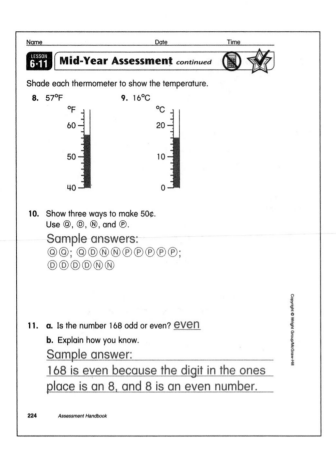

8. 57°F

9. 16°C

10. Show three ways to make 50¢.
Use Ⓠ, Ⓓ, Ⓝ, and Ⓟ.

Sample answers:

ⓆⓆ; ⓆⒹⓃⓃⓅⓅⓅⓅⓅ;

ⒹⒹⒹⒹⓃⓃ

11. a. Is the number 168 odd or even? even

b. Explain how you know.

Sample answer:
168 is even because the digit in the ones
place is an 8, and 8 is an even number.

LESSON 6·11 | **Mid-Year Assessment** *continued*

12. Sally's game mat for the *Money Exchange Game* looks like this:

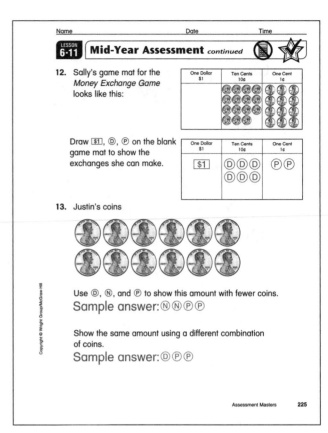

Draw 🅂🄸, Ⓓ, Ⓟ on the blank game mat to show the exchanges she can make.

One Dollar $1	Ten Cents 10¢	One Cent 1¢
$1	ⒹⒹⒹ ⒹⒹⒹ	ⓅⓅ

13. Justin's coins

Use Ⓓ, Ⓝ, and Ⓟ to show this amount with fewer coins.

Sample answer: ⓃⓃⓅⓅ

Show the same amount using a different combination of coins.

Sample answer: ⒹⓅⓅ

LESSON 6·11 | **Mid-Year Assessment** *continued*

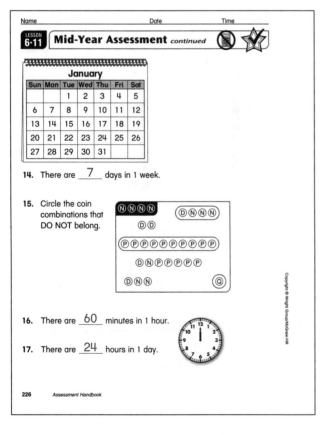

January

Sun	Mon	Tue	Wed	Thu	Fri	Sat
		1	2	3	4	5
6	7	8	9	10	11	12
13	14	15	16	17	18	19
20	21	22	23	24	25	26
27	28	29	30	31		

14. There are __7__ days in 1 week.

15. Circle the coin combinations that DO NOT belong.

16. There are __60__ minutes in 1 hour.

17. There are __24__ hours in 1 day.

LESSON 12·8 | **End-of-Year Assessment**

1. Count by 10s. Start at 2,166.

2,166; __2,176__; __2,186__; __2,196__; __2,206__; __2,216__

2. In 8,603,
the value of 6 is __600__.
the value of 0 is __0__.
the value of 8 is __8,000__.
the value of 3 is __3__.

3. Solve.

			Unit
			fish

a. 56
      +67
      123

b. 342
      +139
      481

c. 64
      −39
       25

d. 256
      −178
       78

4. a. Complete the graph.
Tia read 6 books.
Ian read 3 books.
Theo read 5 books.
Jen read 3 books.

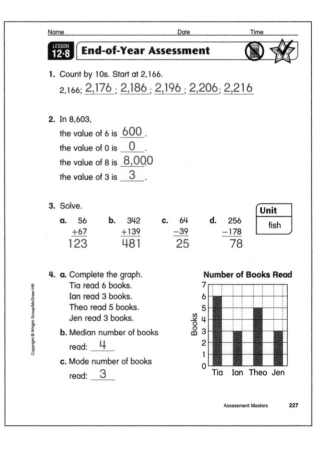

Number of Books Read

b. Median number of books read: __4__

c. Mode number of books read: __3__

LESSON 12·8 **End-of-Year Assessment** *continued*

5. Measure this line segment to the nearest inch and to the nearest centimeter.

<u>4 or 5</u> inches   <u>11</u> centimeters

6. Fill in the oval for the best answer. A second grader may weigh about
- ● 60 pounds.
- ○ 60 ounces.
- ○ 60 feet.
- ○ 60 cups.

7. This is a picture of a
- ○ pyramid.
- ● cylinder.
- ○ rectangular prism.

8. a. Write the name of the shape. Use the words in the box to help you.

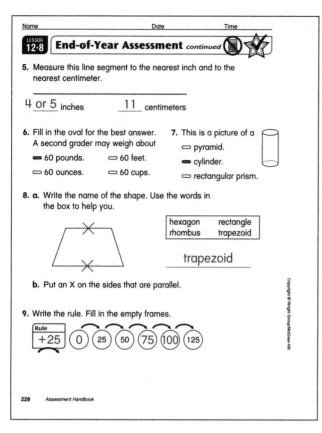

| hexagon | rectangle |
| rhombus | trapezoid |

<u>trapezoid</u>

b. Put an X on the sides that are parallel.

9. Write the rule. Fill in the empty frames.

Rule
+25
(0) (25) (50) (75) (100) (125)

LESSON 12·8 **End-of-Year Assessment** *continued*

10. Use bills and coins to solve.

Ian saved $4.50 for his mother's birthday present. His sister saved $3.40. How much money did they save in all?

a. Answer: <u>$7.90</u>

b. Number model: <u>$4.50 + $3.40 = $7.90;</u>
<u>$3.40 + $4.50 = $7.90</u>

11. Draw an array to match the number story.

5 crayons in each box

2 boxes of crayons

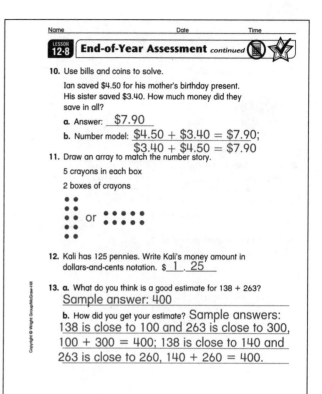

12. Kali has 125 pennies. Write Kali's money amount in dollars-and-cents notation. $ <u>1</u> . <u>25</u>

13. a. What do you think is a good estimate for 138 + 263?
<u>Sample answer: 400</u>

b. How did you get your estimate? Sample answers:
138 is close to 100 and 263 is close to 300,
100 + 300 = 400; 138 is close to 140 and
263 is close to 260, 140 + 260 = 400.

LESSON 12·8 **End-of-Year Assessment** *continued*

14. Write a sentence about something that is likely to happen today.
<u>Sample answer: It is likely that I will eat lunch today.</u>

15. Use the tick marks to draw lines to show square units. Then count the squares to find the area.

Area = <u>15</u> square cm

16. Use =, +, or −.
a. 8 <u>+</u> 6 = 14   **b.** 15 <u>−</u> 5 = 10
c. 25 <u>=</u> 15 + 10   **d.** 18 = 10 <u>+</u> 8

17. What fraction of the circles is shaded? <u>2</u>/<u>5</u> or <u>4</u>/<u>10</u>

●●○○○
●●○○○

18. Complete.
a. 1 week = <u>7</u> days   **b.** <u>24</u> hours = 1 day

19. Shade $\frac{1}{2}$ and write the fraction.

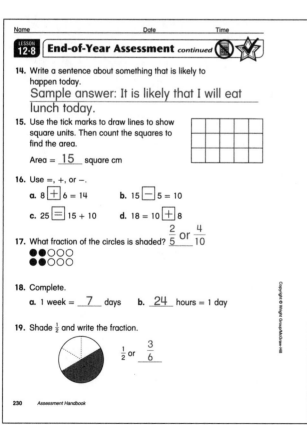

$\frac{1}{2}$ or <u>3</u>/<u>6</u>

LESSON 12·8 **End-of-Year Assessment** *continued*

20. Write the time.

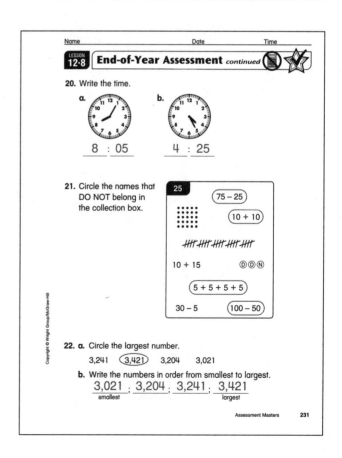

a. 8 : 05   **b.** 4 : 25

21. Circle the names that DO NOT belong in the collection box.

25

(75 − 25)
(10 + 10)
10 + 15   ⓓ ⓓ ⓝ
(5 + 5 + 5 + 5)
30 − 5   (100 − 50)

22. a. Circle the largest number.
3,241   (3,421)   3,204   3,021

b. Write the numbers in order from smallest to largest.
<u>3,021</u> ; <u>3,204</u> ; <u>3,241</u> ; <u>3,421</u>
smallest   largest

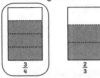 **End-of-Year Assessment** *continued*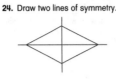

23. Circle the larger fraction.   **24.** Draw two lines of symmetry.

$\frac{3}{4}$ $\frac{2}{3}$

25. Fill in the diagram if needed.

Fish P weighs 36 pounds.
Fish M weighs 22 pounds.
How much more does Fish P weigh?

Fish P weighs __14__ pounds more.

Quantity
36

Quantity	
22	__14__
	Difference

26. Use counters or drawings to solve.

a. 15 stickers, 3 children

How many stickers per child? __5__ stickers

b. 40 candies, 4 candies per child

How many children? __10__ children

27. Write two addition facts for the fact triangle.

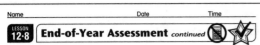

$$\frac{7}{} + \frac{9}{} = \frac{16}{}$$
$$\frac{9}{} + \frac{7}{} = \frac{16}{}$$

Individual Profile of Progress

Name _____ Date _____

Lesson	Recognizing Student Achievement	A.P.*	Comments
1◆1	**Write and order numbers.** [Number and Numeration Goal 7]		
1◆2	**Count coin combinations.** [Operations and Computation Goal 2]		
1◆3	**Tell time to the nearest half-hour.** [Measurement and Reference Frames Goal 6]		
1◆4	**Know basic addition facts.** [Operations and Computation Goal 1]		
1◆5	**Count bill combinations.** [Operations and Computation Goal 2]		
1◆6	**Solve sum-equals-ten facts.** [Operations and Computation Goal 1]		
1◆7	**Complete and describe a number pattern.** [Patterns, Functions, and Algebra Goal 1]		
1◆8	**Solve number-grid puzzles using number-grid patterns.** [Patterns, Functions, and Algebra Goal 1]		
1◆9	**Use number models to write equivalent names for numbers.** [Number and Numeration Goal 5]		
1◆10	**Calculate the value of coin combinations.** [Operations and Computation Goal 2]		
1◆11	**Compare numbers.** [Number and Numeration Goal 7]		
1◆12	**Identify odd and even numbers.** [Number and Numeration Goal 4]		

*****Assess Progress:**  = adequate progress   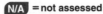 = not adequate progress   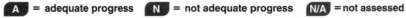 = not assessed

Go to *www.everydaymathonline.com* for digital checklists.

Individual Profile of Progress

Name _____ Date _____

Problem(s)	Progress Check 1	A.P.*	Comments
Oral/Slate Assessment			
1	**Count up by 2s beginning with 0, 10, 26, and 50.** [Number and Numeration Goal 1]		
2	**Count up by 5s beginning with 0, 15, 45, and 70.** [Number and Numeration Goal 1]		
3	**Count up by 10s beginning with 0, 40, and 60.** [Number and Numeration Goal 1]		
4	**Write the number that is ten more than (or ten less than) 15; 29; 72; 100.** [Number and Numeration Goal 1; Patterns, Functions, and Algebra Goal 1]		
5	**Write another name for the number 20; 25; 50.** [Number and Numeration Goal 5]		
Written Assessment Part A			
1	**Show 12 with tally marks.** [Number and Numeration Goal 5]		
2	**Find the value of a collection of coins.** [Operations and Computation Goal 2]		
3	**Fill in the missing numbers on a number line.** [Number and Numeration Goal 1]		
4	**Write three names for 10.** [Number and Numeration Goal 5]		
5	**Write the time. Draw hands to show 7:30.** [Measurement and Reference Frames Goal 6]		
6	**Solve number-grid puzzles.** [Patterns, Functions, and Algebra Goal 1]		
Written Assessment Part B			
7–9	**Solve problems with addition facts.** [Operations and Computation Goal 1]		
10	**Show four ways to make 25¢.** [Operations and Computation Goal 2]		
11	**Write the number that is 10 less and 10 more.** [Patterns, Functions, and Algebra Goal 1]		

*Assess Progress:  **A** = adequate progress   **N** = not adequate progress   **N/A** = not assessed   **Formative Assessments**

Class _____

Date _____

Names	1·1	1·2	1·3	1·4	1·5	1·6	1·7	1·8	1·9	1·10	1·11	1·12
	Write and order numbers. [Number and Numeration Goal 7]	**Count coin combinations.** [Operations and Computation Goal 2]	**Tell time to the nearest half-hour.** [Measurement and Reference Frames Goal 6]	**Know basic addition facts.** [Operations and Computation Goal 1]	**Count bill combinations.** [Operations and Computation Goal 1]	**Solve sum-equals-ten facts.** [Operations and Computation Goal 1]	**Complete and describe a number pattern.** [Patterns, Functions, and Algebra Goal 1]	**Solve number-grid puzzles using number-grid patterns.** [Patterns, Functions, and Algebra Goal 1]	**Use number models to write equivalent names for numbers.** [Number and Numeration Goal 5]	**Calculate the value of coin combinations.** [Operations and Computation Goal 2]	**Compare numbers.** [Number and Numeration Goal 7]	**Identify odd and even numbers.** [Number and Numeration Goal 4]
1.												
2.												
3.												
4.												
5.												
6.												
7.												
8.												
9.												
10.												
11.												
12.												
13.												
14.												
15.												
16.												
17.												
18.												
19.												
20.												
21.												
22.												
23.												
24.												
25.												

Assess Progress: = adequate progress = not adequate progress = not assessed

Class _____

Date _____

Names	Oral/Slate					Written — Part A						Written — Part B		
	1. Count up by 2s beginning with 0, 10, 26, and 50. [Number and Numeration Goal 1]	2. Count up by 5s beginning with 0, 15, 45, and 70. [Number and Numeration Goal 1]	3. Count up by 10s beginning with 0, 40, and 60. [Number and Numeration Goal 1]	4. Write the number that is ten more than (or ten less than) 15; 29; 72; 100. [Number and Numeration Goal 1; Patterns, Functions, and Algebra Goal 1]	5. Write another name for the number 20; 25; 50. [Number and Numeration Goal 5]	1. Show 12 with tally marks. [Number and Numeration Goal 5]	2. Find the value of a collection of coins. [Operations and Computation Goal 2]	3. Fill in the missing numbers on a number line. [Number and Numeration Goal 1]	4. Write three names for 10. [Number and Numeration Goal 5]	5. Write the time. Draw hands to show 7:30. [Measurement and Reference Frames Goal 6]	6. Solve number-grid puzzles. [Patterns, Functions, and Algebra Goal 1]	7–9. Solve problems with addition facts. [Operations and Computation Goal 1]	10. Show four ways to make 25¢. [Operations and Computation Goal 2]	11. Write the number that is 10 less and 10 more. [Patterns, Functions, and Algebra Goal 1]
1.														
2.														
3.														
4.														
5.														
6.														
7.														
8.														
9.														
10.														
11.														
12.														
13.														
14.														
15.														
16.														
17.														
18.														
19.														
20.														
21.														
22.														
23.														
24.														
25.														

Assess Progress: **A** = adequate progress **N** = not adequate progress **N/A** = not assessed **Formative Assessments**

Individual Profile of Progress

Name _____ Date _____

Lesson	Recognizing Student Achievement	A.P.*	Comments
2◆1	**Write a number story.** [Operations and Computation Goal 4]		
2◆2	**Recall math facts more quickly than a calculator.** [Operations and Computation Goal 1]		
2◆3	**Count back by 5s.** [Number and Numeration Goal 1]		
2◆4	**Recall math facts more quickly than a calculator.** [Operations and Computation Goal 1]		
2◆5	**Know doubles facts.** [Operations and Computation Goal 1]		
2◆6	**Write fact families for dominoes.** [Patterns, Functions, and Algebra Goal 3]		
2◆7	**Write a number story to describe a number sentence.** [Patterns, Functions, and Algebra Goal 2]		
2◆8	**Use counting patterns on the number grid.** [Patterns, Functions, and Algebra Goal 1]		
2◆9	**Write number sentences and generate equivalent names for a given number.** [Number and Numeration Goal 5]		
2◆10	**Extend a numeric pattern using addition and subtraction.** [Patterns, Functions, and Algebra Goal 1]		
2◆11	**Solve "What's My Rule?" problems using addition and subtraction with a known rule.** [Patterns, Functions, and Algebra Goal 1]		
2◆12	**Write a fact family from a Fact Triangle.** [Operations and Computation Goal 1]		
2◆13	**Write a number story for a number model.** [Patterns, Functions, and Algebra Goal 2]		

*Assess Progress: **A** = adequate progress   **N** = not adequate progress   **N/A** = not assessed

Go to *www.everydaymathonline.com* for digital checklists.

Unit 2 Individual Profile of Progress

Name _____ Date _____

Problem(s)	Progress Check 2	A.P.*	Comments
Oral/Slate Assessment			
1	**Read the numbers 34, 82, and 96 orally.** [Number and Numeration Goal 2]		
2	**Read the numbers 340, 995, and 109 orally.** [Number and Numeration Goal 2]		
3	**Solve a word problem involving addition.** [Operations and Computation Goal 1]		
4	**Solve a word problem involving addition.** [Operations and Computation Goal 1]		
Written Assessment Part A			
1	**Add and write the turnaround.** [Patterns, Functions, and Algebra Goal 3]		
2	**Write the fact family for 2, 11, and 9.** [Operations and Computation Goal 1]		
3	**Add.** [Operations and Computation Goal 1]		
4	**Subtract.** [Operations and Computation Goal 1]		
5	**Fill in the empty frames.** [Patterns, Functions, and Algebra Goal 1]		
Written Assessment Part B			
6	**Circle the names for 14.** [Number and Numeration Goal 5]		
7	**Find the rule and complete the table.** [Patterns, Functions, and Algebra Goal 1]		
8	**Add.** [Operations and Computation Goal 1]		
9	**Subtract.** [Operations and Computation Goal 1]		
10	**Put an X on the number in the tens place.** [Number and Numeration Goal 2]		
11	**Show $1.00 two ways using Q, D, N.** [Operations and Computation Goal 2]		
12	**Use the graph to answer the questions.** [Data and Chance Goal 2]		

*Assess Progress: **A** = adequate progress **N** = not adequate progress **N/A** = not assessed Formative Assessments

Go to *www.everydaymathonline.com* for digital checklists. Individual Profile of Progress **241**

Class Checklist:
Recognizing Student Achievement

Class _____

Date _____

Names	Write a number story. [Operations and Computation Goal 4] 2·1	Recall math facts more quickly than a calculator. [Operations and Computation Goal 1] 2·2	Count back by 5s. [Number and Numeration Goal 1] 2·3	Recall math facts more quickly than a calculator. [Operations and Computation Goal 1] 2·4	Know doubles facts. [Operations and Computation Goal 1] 2·5	Write fact families for dominoes. [Patterns, Functions, and Algebra Goal 3] 2·6	Write a number story to describe a number sentence. [Patterns, Functions, and Algebra Goal 2] 2·7	Use counting patterns on the number grid. [Patterns, Functions, and Algebra Goal 1] 2·8	Write number sentences and generate equivalent names for a given number. [Number and Numeration Goal 5] 2·9	Extend a numeric pattern using addition and subtraction. [Patterns, Functions, and Algebra Goal 1] 2·10	Solve "What's My Rule?" problems using addition and subtraction with a known rule. [Patterns, Functions, and Algebra Goal 1] 2·11	Write a fact family from a Fact Triangle. [Operations and Computation Goal 1] 2·12	Write a number story for a number model. [Patterns, Functions, and Algebra Goal 2] 2·13
1.													
2.													
3.													
4.													
5.													
6.													
7.													
8.													
9.													
10.													
11.													
12.													
13.													
14.													
15.													
16.													
17.													
18.													
19.													
20.													
21.													
22.													
23.													
24.													
25.													

Assess Progress: = adequate progress = not adequate progress = not assessed

Class _____

Date _____

Written

	Oral/Slate				Part A					Part B						

Column headers:

1. **Read the numbers 34, 82, and 96 orally.** [Number and Numeration Goal 2]
2. **Read the numbers 340, 995, and 109 orally.** [Number and Numeration Goal 2]
3. **Solve a word problem involving addition.** [Operations and Computation Goal 1]
4. **Solve a word problem involving addition.** [Operations and Computation Goal 1]
1. **Add and write the turnaround.** [Patterns, Functions, and Algebra Goal 3]
2. **Write the fact family for 2, 11, and 9.** [Operations and Computation Goal 1]
3. **Add.** [Operations and Computation Goal 1]
4. **Subtract.** [Operations and Computation Goal 1]
5. **Fill in the empty frames.** [Patterns, Functions, and Algebra Goal 1]
6. **Circle the names for 14.** [Number and Numeration Goal 5]
7. **Find the rule and complete the table.** [Patterns, Functions, and Algebra Goal 1]
8. **Add.** [Operations and Computation Goal 1]
9. **Subtract.** [Operations and Computation Goal 1]
10. **Put an X on the number in the tens place.** [Number and Numeration Goal 2]
11. **Show $1.00 two ways using Q, D, N.** [Operations and Computation Goal 2]
12. **Use the graph to answer the questions.** [Data and Chance Goal 2]

Names
1.
2.
3.
4.
5.
6.
7.
8.
9.
10.
11.
12.
13.
14.
15.
16.
17.
18.
19.
20.
21.
22.
23.
24.
25.

Assess Progress: **A** = adequate progress **N** = not adequate progress **N/A** = not assessed **Formative Assessments**

Go to *www.everydaymathonline.com* for digital checklists.

Class Checklist **243**

Individual Profile of Progress

Name _____ Date _____

Lesson	Recognizing Student Achievement	A.P.*	Comments
3•1	**Write numbers shown with base-10 blocks.** [Number and Numeration Goal 2]		
3•2	**Show coin combinations.** [Operations and Computation Goal 2]		
3•3	**Record tally marks for a given number.** [Number and Numeration Goal 5]		
3•4	**Show time to the nearest half-hour.** [Measurement and Reference Frames Goal 6]		
3•5	**Show equivalent names for 20.** [Number and Numeration Goal 5]		
3•6	**Create number patterns and rules in Frames-and-Arrows problems.** [Patterns, Functions, and Algebra Goal 1]		
3•7	**Make the largest number from two digits.** [Number and Numeration Goal 2]		
3•8	**Calculate the value of coin combinations.** [Operations and Computation Goal 2]		

*Assess Progress: 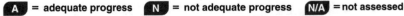 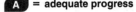 **A** = adequate progress **N** = not adequate progress 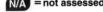 **N/A** = not assessed

Go to *www.everydaymathonline.com* for digital checklists.

Individual Profile of Progress

Name _____ Date _____

Problem(s)	Progress Check 3	A.P.*	Comments
Oral/Slate Assessment			
1	**Read the numbers 57, 101, and 220 aloud.** [Number and Numeration Goal 2]		
2	**Count by 5s, 10s, 25s, and 100s.** [Number and Numeration Goal 1]		
3	**Write numbers as shown using base-10 blocks.** [Number and Numeration Goal 2]		
4	**Identify place values in 2- and 3-digit numbers.** [Number and Numeration Goal 2]		
Written Assessment Part A			
1	**Show coins for 27¢.** [Operations and Computation Goal 2]		
2	**Know addition facts.** [Operations and Computation Goal 1]		
3	**Count by 5s.** [Number and Numeration Goal 1]		
4	**Interpret a picture graph.** [Data and Chance Goal 2]		
5	**Solve an addition number-story problem.** [Operations and Computation Goal 4]		
Written Assessment Part B			
6	**Solve a Frames-and-Arrows problem with 2 rules.** [Patterns, Functions, and Algebra Goal 1]		
7	**Solve extended addition facts.** [Operations and Computation Goal 1]		
8	**Add or subtract 2-digit numbers.** [Operations and Computation Goal 2]		
9	**Make change.** [Operations and Computation Goal 2]		
10	**Count by 25s.** [Number and Numeration Goal 1]		
11	**Interpret a bar graph.** [Data and Chance Goal 2]		
12	**Read a thermometer.** [Measurement and Reference Frames Goal 5]		

*Assess Progress:  **A** = adequate progress **N** = not adequate progress **N/A** = not assessed  **Formative Assessments**

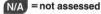

Class Checklist:
Recognizing Student Achievement

Class _____

Date _____

Names	Write numbers shown with base-10 blocks. [Number and Numeration Goal 2] 3·1	Show coin combinations. [Operations and Computation Goal 2] 3·2	Record tally marks for a given number. [Number and Numeration Goal 5] 3·3	Show time to the nearest half-hour. [Measurement and Reference Frames Goal 6] 3·4	Show equivalent names for 20. [Number and Numeration Goal 5] 3·5	Create number patterns and rules in Frames-and-Arrows problems. [Patterns, Functions, and Algebra Goal 1] 3·6	Make the largest number from two digits. [Number and Numeration Goal 2] 3·7	Calculate the value of coin combinations. [Operations and Computation Goal 2] 3·8
1.								
2.								
3.								
4.								
5.								
6.								
7.								
8.								
9.								
10.								
11.								
12.								
13.								
14.								
15.								
16.								
17.								
18.								
19.								
20.								
21.								
22.								
23.								
24.								
25.								

Assess Progress: **A** = adequate progress **N** = not adequate progress **N/A** = not assessed

Go to *www.everydaymathonline.com* for digital checklists.

Class Checklist:
Progress Check 3

Class _____

Date _____

Names	Oral/Slate				Written Part A					Written Part B							
	1. Read the numbers 57, 101, and 220 aloud. [Number and Numerations Goal 2]	2. Count by 5s, 10s, 25s, and 100s. [Number and Numeration Goal 1]	3. Write numbers as shown using base-10 blocks. [Number and Numeration Goal 2]	4. Identify place values in 2- and 3-digit numbers. [Number and Numeration Goal 2]	1. Show coins for 27¢. [Operations and Computation Goal 2]	2. Know addition facts. [Operations and Computation Goal 1]	3. Count by 5s. [Number and Numeration Goal 1]	4. Interpret a picture graph. [Data and Chance Goal 2]	5. Solve an addition number-story problem. [Operations and Computation Goal 4]	6. Solve a Frames-and-Arrows problem with 2 rules. [Patterns, Functions, and Algebra Goal 1]	7. Solve extended addition facts. [Operations and Computation Goal 1]	8. Add or subtract 2-digit numbers. [Operations and Computation Goal 2]	9. Make change. [Operations and Computation Goal 2]	10. Count by 25s. [Number and Numeration Goal 1]	11. Interpret a bar graph. [Data and Chance Goal 2]	12. Read a thermometer. [Measurement and Reference Frames Goal 5]
1.																
2.																
3.																
4.																
5.																
6.																
7.																
8.																
9.																
10.																
11.																
12.																
13.																
14.																
15.																
16.																
17.																
18.																
19.																
20.																
21.																
22.																
23.																
24.																
25.																

Assess Progress: **A** = adequate progress   **N** = not adequate progress   **N/A** = not assessed   **Formative Assessments**

Individual Profile of Progress

Name _____ **Date** _____

Lesson	Recognizing Student Achievement	A.P.*	Comments
4•1	**Solve number stories.** [Operations and Computation Goal 4]		
4•2	**Solve parts-and-total situations.** [Operations and Computation Goal 4]		
4•3	**Write equivalent names for $1.00.** [Number and Numeration Goal 5]		
4•4	**Read, show temperatures, and solve temperature-change problems.** [Measurement and Reference Frames Goal 5]		
4•5	**Estimate the total cost of two items.** [Operations and Computation Goal 3]		
4•6	**Tell time to the nearest quarter-hour.** [Measurement and Reference Frames Goal 6]		
4•7	**Record addition facts.** [Operations and Computation Goal 1]		
4•8	**Make ballpark estimates.** [Operations and Computation Goal 3]		
4•9	**Solve problems involving addition of multidigit multiples of ten.** [Operations and Computation Goal 2]		

*__Assess Progress:__  **A** = adequate progress   **N** = not adequate progress   **N/A** = not assessed

Go to _www.everydaymathonline.com_ for digital checklists.

Individual Profile of Progress

Name _____   Date _____

Problem(s)	Progress Check 4	A.P.*	Comments
Oral/Slate Assessment			
1–3	Identify sensible measures in given temperature situations using the Class Thermometer Poster. [Measurement and Reference Frames Goal 5]		
4	Write the sum for 20 + 9. [Operations and Computation Goal 2]		
5	Write the sum for 30 + 8. [Operations and Computation Goal 2]		
6	Write the sum for 2 + 30. [Operations and Computation Goal 2]		
7	Write the sum for 60 + 9. [Operations and Computation Goal 2]		
Written Assessment Part A			
1	Calculate the value of a coin combination. [Operations and Computation Goal 2]		
2a, 2b	Write the temperature. [Measurement and Reference Frames Goal 5]		
3a, 3b	Write whole numbers using standard base-ten notation. [Number and Numeration Goal 2]		
4a–4d	Recognize numbers as odd or even. [Number and Numeration Goals 4 and 6]		
5	Fill in the number-grid puzzle. [Patterns, Functions, and Algebra Goal 1]		
Written Assessment Part B			
6	Calculate the amount of change. [Measurement and Reference Frames Goal 4]		
7	Solve the change-to-less problem. [Operations and Computation Goal 2]		
8a, 9a, 10a	Solve problems using ballpark estimates. [Operations and Computation Goal 3]		
8b, 9b, 10b	Solve problems using multidigit addition. [Operations and Computation Goal 2]		
11, 12	Mark each thermometer to show the temperature. [Measurement and Reference Frames Goal 5]		
13	Circle the digit in the 100s place. [Number and Numeration Goal 2]		

*Assess Progress: **A** = adequate progress   **N** = not adequate progress   **N/A** = not assessed   Formative Assessments

Go to *www.everydaymathonline.com* for digital checklists.

Class _____

Date _____

Names	Solve number stories. [Operations and Computation Goal 4] 4·1	Solve parts-and-total situations. [Operations and Computation Goal 4] 4·2	Write equivalent names for $1.00. [Number and Numeration Goal 5] 4·3	Read, show temperatures, and solve temperature-change problems. [Measurement and Reference Frames Goal 5] 4·4	Estimate the total cost of two items. [Operations and Computation Goal 3] 4·5	Tell time to the nearest quarter-hour. [Measurement and Reference Frames Goal 6] 4·6	Record addition facts. [Operations and Computation Goal 1] 4·7	Make ballpark estimates. [Operations and Computation Goal 3] 4·8	Solve problems involving addition of multidigit multiples of ten. [Operations and Computation Goal 2] 4·9
1.									
2.									
3.									
4.									
5.									
6.									
7.									
8.									
9.									
10.									
11.									
12.									
13.									
14.									
15.									
16.									
17.									
18.									
19.									
20.									
21.									
22.									
23.									
24.									
25.									

Assess Progress:  **A** = adequate progress   **N** = not adequate progress   **N/A** = not assessed

Go to *www.everydaymathonline.com* for digital checklists.

Class _____

Date _____

	Oral/Slate				Written Part A					Part B						
Names	1–3. Identify sensible measures in given temperature situations using the Class Thermometer Poster. [Measurement and Reference Frames Goal 5]	4. Write the sum for 20 + 9. [Operations and Computation Goal 2]	5. Write the sum for 30 + 8. [Operations and Computation Goal 2]	6. Write the sum for 2 + 30. [Operations and Computation Goal 2]	7. Write the sum for 60 + 9. [Operations and Computation Goal 2]	1. Calculate the value of a coin combination. [Operations and Computation Goal 2]	2a, 2b. Write the temperature. [Measurement and Reference Frames Goal 5]	3a, 3b. Write whole numbers using standard base-ten notation. [Number and Numeration Goal 2]	4a–4d. Recognize numbers as odd or even. [Number and Numeration Goals 4 and 6]	5. Fill in the number-grid puzzle. [Patterns, Functions, and Algebra Goal 1]	6. Calculate the amount of change. [Measurement and Reference Frames Goal 4]	7. Solve the change-to-less problem. [Operations and Computation Goal 2]	8a, 9a, 10a. Solve problems using ballpark estimates. [Operations and Computation Goal 3]	8b, 9b, 10b. Solve problems using multidigit addition. [Operations and Computation Goal 2]	11, 12. Mark each thermometer to show the temperature. [Measurement and Reference Frames Goal 5]	13. Circle the digit in the 100s place. [Number and Numeration Goal 2]
1.																
2.																
3.																
4.																
5.																
6.																
7.																
8.																
9.																
10.																
11.																
12.																
13.																
14.																
15.																
16.																
17.																
18.																
19.																
20.																
21.																
22.																
23.																
24.																
25.																

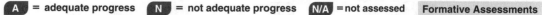

Assess Progress: **A** = adequate progress   **N** = not adequate progress   **N/A** = not assessed   **Formative Assessments**

Go to *www.everydaymathonline.com* for digital checklists.

Individual Profile of Progress

Name _____   Date _____

Lesson	Recognizing Student Achievement	A.P.*	Comments
5◆1	**Read the time and match it to its digital notation.** [Measurement and Reference Frames Goal 6]		
5◆2	**Use a straightedge to draw a line segment.** [Geometry Goal 1]		
5◆3	**Identify parallel lines.** [Geometry Goal 1]		
5◆4	**Name 2-dimensional shapes.** [Geometry Goal 2]		
5◆5	**Use ballpark estimates for addition problems.** [Operations and Computation Goal 3]		
5◆6	**Find the difference between two 2-digit numbers.** [Operations and Computation Goal 2]		
5◆7	**Complete patterns in a number grid.** [Patterns, Functions, and Algebra Goal 1]		
5◆8	**Complete 2-dimensional symmetric shapes.** [Geometry Goal 3]		

*Assess Progress: **A** = adequate progress   **N** = not adequate progress   **N/A** = not assessed

Individual Profile of Progress

Unit 5

Name _____ Date _____

Problem(s)	Progress Check 5	A.P.*	Comments
Oral/Slate Assessment			
1	**Respond to a number with its 100-complement.** [Operations and Computation Goal 2]		
2	**State sums of given extended addition facts.** [Operations and Computation Goal 2]		
3	**Record times shown on a demonstration clock.** [Measurement and Reference Frames Goal 6]		
4	**Solve basic addition facts.** [Operations and Computation Goal 1]		
Written Assessment Part A			
1	**Write the fact family.** [Operations and Computation Goal 1]		
2	**Count in the thousands.** [Number and Numeration Goal 1]		
3	**Order whole numbers in the 100s and 1,000s.** [Number and Numeration Goal 7]		
4	**Draw line segments.** [Geometry Goal 1]		
5–7	**Identify 2- and 3-dimensional figures.** [Geometry Goal 2]		
Written Assessment Part B			
8, 9	**Identify 3-dimensional figures.** [Geometry Goal 2]		
10	**Draw a line segment.** [Geometry Goal 1]		
11, 12	**Draw parallel and nonparallel line segments.** [Geometry Goal 1]		
13	**Draw lines of symmetry.** [Geometry Goal 3]		

*Assess Progress: **A** = adequate progress **N** = not adequate progress **N/A** = not assessed   **Formative Assessments**

Go to *www.everydaymathonline.com* for digital checklists.

Class Checklist:
Recognizing Student Achievement

Unit 5

Class _____

Date _____

Names	5·1 Read the time and match it to its digital notation. [Measurement and Reference Frames Goal 6]	5·2 Use a straightedge to draw a line segment. [Geometry Goal 1]	5·3 Identify parallel lines. [Geometry Goal 1]	5·4 Name 2-dimensional shapes. [Geometry Goal 2]	5·5 Use ballpark estimates for addition problems. [Operations and Computation Goal 3]	5·6 Find the difference between two 2-digit numbers. [Operations and Computation Goal 2]	5·7 Complete patterns in a number grid. [Patterns, Functions, and Algebra Goal 1]	5·8 Complete 2-dimensional symmetric shapes. [Geometry Goal 3]
1.								
2.								
3.								
4.								
5.								
6.								
7.								
8.								
9.								
10.								
11.								
12.								
13.								
14.								
15.								
16.								
17.								
18.								
19.								
20.								
21.								
22.								
23.								
24.								
25.								

Assess Progress: **A** = adequate progress   **N** = not adequate progress   **N/A** = not assessed

Go to *www.everydaymathonline.com* for digital checklists.

Class _____

Date _____

Names	Oral/Slate				Written Part A					Part B			
	1. Respond to a number with its 100-complement. [Operations and Computation Goal 2]	2. State sums of given extended addition facts. [Operations and Computation Goal 2]	3. Record times shown on a demonstration clock. [Measurement and Reference Frames Goal 6]	4. Solve basic addition facts. [Operations and Computation Goal 1]	1. Write the fact family. [Operations and Computation Goal 1]	2. Count in the thousands. [Number and Numeration Goal 1]	3. Order whole numbers in the 100s and 1,000s. [Number and Numeration Goal 7]	4. Draw line segments. [Geometry Goal 1]	5–7. Identify 2- and 3-dimensional figures. [Geometry Goal 2]	8, 9. Identify 3-dimensional figures. [Geometry Goal 2]	10. Draw a line segment. [Geometry Goal 1]	11, 12. Draw parallel and nonparallel line segments. [Geometry Goal 1]	13. Draw lines of symmetry. [Geometry Goal 3]
1.													
2.													
3.													
4.													
5.													
6.													
7.													
8.													
9.													
10.													
11.													
12.													
13.													
14.													
15.													
16.													
17.													
18.													
19.													
20.													
21.													
22.													
23.													
24.													
25.													

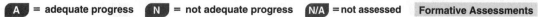

Assess Progress: **A** = adequate progress   **N** = not adequate progress   **N/A** = not assessed   **Formative Assessments**

Individual Profile of Progress

Name _____ Date _____

Lesson	Recognizing Student Achievement	A.P.*	Comments
6◆1	**Add three and four numbers.** [Operations and Computation Goal 2]		
6◆2	**Solve comparison number stories.** [Operations and Computation Goal 4]		
6◆3	**Read graphs.** [Data and Chance Goal 2]		
6◆4	**Solve number stories.** [Operations and Computation Goal 2]		
6◆5	**Use probability language.** [Data and Chance Goal 3]		
6◆6	**Create $1.00 using different coin combinations.** [Measurement and Reference Frames Goal 4]		
6◆7	**Combine equal groups to find the total.** [Operations and Computation Goal 4]		
6◆8	**Draw rectangular arrays.** [Operations and Computation Goal 4]		
6◆9	**Draw and measure a 3-inch line segment.** [Measurement and Reference Frames Goal 1]		
6◆10	**Use counters and drawings to solve equal-sharing problems.** [Operations and Computation Goal 4]		

*Assess Progress:  **A** = adequate progress **N** = not adequate progress **N/A** = not assessed

Individual Profile of Progress

Name _____   Date _____

Problem(s)	Progress Check 6	A.P.*	Comments
Oral/Slate Assessment			
1–2	**Solve a word problem involving basic multiplication facts.** [Operations and Computation Goal 4]		
3–6	**Solve multidigit addition problems.** [Operations and Computation Goal 2]		
Written Assessment Part A			
1	**Write the time.** [Measurement and Reference Frames Goal 6]		
2	**Solve a parts-and-total situation.** [Operations and Computation Goal 4]		
3	**Complete the "What's My Rule?" table.** [Patterns, Functions, and Algebra Goal 1]		
4	**Use the >, <, and = symbols.** [Patterns, Functions, and Algebra Goal 2]		
Written Assessment Part B			
5	**Make ballpark estimates.** [Operations and Computation Goal 3]		
6	**Use arrays to model multiplication.** [Operations and Computation Goal 4]		
7	**Solve a comparison situation.** [Operations and Computation Goal 4]		
8–10	**Solve multidigit subtraction problems.** [Operations and Computation Goal 2]		

*Assess Progress: **A** = adequate progress   **N** = not adequate progress   **N/A** = not assessed   **Formative Assessments**

Class Checklist:
Recognizing Student Achievement

Class _____

Date _____

Names	Add three and four numbers. [Operations and Computation Goal 2]	Solve comparison number stories. [Operations and Computation Goal 4]	Read graphs. [Data and Chance Goal 2]	Solve number stories. [Operations and Computation Goal 2]	Use probability language. [Data and Chance Goal 3]	Create $1.00 using different coin combinations. [Measurement and Reference Frames Goal 4]	Combine equal groups to find the total. [Operations and Computation Goal 4]	Draw rectangular arrays. [Operations and Computation Goal 4]	Draw and measure a 3-inch line segment. [Measurement and Reference Frames Goal 1]	Use counters and drawings to solve equal-sharing problems. [Operations and Computation Goal 4]
	6·1	6·2	6·3	6·4	6·5	6·6	6·7	6·8	6·9	6·10
1.										
2.										
3.										
4.										
5.										
6.										
7.										
8.										
9.										
10.										
11.										
12.										
13.										
14.										
15.										
16.										
17.										
18.										
19.										
20.										
21.										
22.										
23.										
24.										
25.										

Assess Progress: **A** = adequate progress   **N** = not adequate progress   **N/A** = not assessed

Class Checklist:
Progress Check 6

Class _____

Date _____

Names	Oral/Slate		Written Part A				Written Part B			
	1–2. Solve a word problem involving basic multiplication facts. [Operations and Computation Goal 4]	3–6. Solve multidigit addition problems. [Operations and Computation Goal 2]	1. Write the time. [Measurement and Reference Frames Goal 6]	2. Solve a parts-and-total situation. [Operations and Computation Goal 4]	3. Complete the "What's My Rule?" table. [Patterns, Functions, and Algebra Goal 1]	4. Use the >, <, and = symbols. [Patterns, Functions, and Algebra Goal 2]	5. Make ballpark estimates. [Operations and Computation Goal 3]	6. Use arrays to model multiplication. [Operations and Computation Goal 4]	7. Solve a comparison situation. [Operations and Computation Goal 4]	8–10. Solve multidigit subtraction problems. [Operations and Computation Goal 2]
1.										
2.										
3.										
4.										
5.										
6.										
7.										
8.										
9.										
10.										
11.										
12.										
13.										
14.										
15.										
16.										
17.										
18.										
19.										
20.										
21.										
22.										
23.										
24.										
25.										

Assess Progress: **A** = adequate progress **N** = not adequate progress **N/A** = not assessed **Formative Assessments**

Go to *www.everydaymathonline.com* for digital checklists.

Individual Profile of Progress

Name _____ Date _____

Lesson	Recognizing Student Achievement	A.P.*	Comments
7◆1	**Count by 2s.** [Number and Numeration Goal 1]		
7◆2	**Find the difference between 2-digit numbers and any higher multiple of 10.** [Operations and Computation Goal 2]		
7◆3	**Solve addition problems with multiple addends.** [Operations and Computation Goal 2]		
7◆4	**Use a rule to follow a pattern.** [Patterns, Functions, and Algebra Goal 1]		
7◆5	**Draw a 5-by-3 array.** [Operations and Computation Goal 4]		
7◆6	**Compare standard and metric units of length.** [Measurement and Reference Frames Goal 1]		
7◆7	**Tell time to the quarter-hour.** [Measurement and Reference Frames Goal 6]		
7◆8	**Find the median.** [Data and Chance Goal 2]		

*Assess Progress:  **A** = adequate progress    **N** = not adequate progress   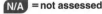 **N/A** = not assessed

Name _____   Date _____

Problem(s)	Progress Check 7	A.P.*	Comments
Oral/Slate Assessment			
1–3	**Solve equal-groups number stories.** [Operations and Computation Goal 4]		
4–6	**Solve multidigit addition problems.** [Operations and Computation Goal 2]		
Written Assessment Part A			
1a	**Solve a multidigit number story.** [Operations and Computation Goal 2]		
1b	**Write a number model.** [Patterns, Functions, and Algebra Goal 2]		
2	**Use data to make a bar graph.** [Data and Chance Goal 1]		
3	**Find the rule for functions involving doubling.** [Patterns, Functions, and Algebra Goal 1]		
4–6	**Identify 3-dimensional shapes.** [Geometry Goal 2]		
7	**Solve multidigit addition problems with 3 or more addends.** [Operations and Computation Goal 2]		
Written Assessment Part B			
8	**Solve "What's My Rule?" with halving.** [Patterns, Functions, and Algebra Goal 1]		
9, 10	**Order numbers and find median and mode.** [Data and Chance Goal 2]		
11	**Fill in missing numbers on a number grid.** [Patterns, Functions, and Algebra Goal 1]		

***Assess Progress:** **A** = adequate progress **N** = not adequate progress **N/A** = not assessed   **Formative Assessments**

Class Checklist:
Recognizing Student Achievement

Class _____

Date _____

Names	Count by 2s. [Number and Numeration Goal 1]	Find the difference between 2-digit numbers and any higher multiple of 10. [Operations and Computation Goal 2]	Solve addition problems with multiple addends. [Operations and Computation Goal 2]	Use a rule to follow a pattern. [Patterns, Functions, and Algebra Goal 1]	Draw a 5-by-3 array. [Operations and Computation Goal 4]	Compare standard and metric units of length. [Measurement and Reference Frames Goal 1]	Tell time to the quarter-hour. [Measurement and Reference Frames Goal 6]	Find the median. [Data and Chance Goal 2]
	7·1	**7·2**	**7·3**	**7·4**	**7·5**	**7·6**	**7·7**	**7·8**
1.								
2.								
3.								
4.								
5.								
6.								
7.								
8.								
9.								
10.								
11.								
12.								
13.								
14.								
15.								
16.								
17.								
18.								
19.								
20.								
21.								
22.								
23.								
24.								
25.								

Assess Progress:  **A** = adequate progress   **N** = not adequate progress   **N/A** = not assessed

Class Checklist:
Progress Check 7

Class _____

Date _____

Names	Oral/Slate		Written Part A							Part B		
	1–3. Solve equal-group number stories. [Operations and Computation Goal 4]	4–6. Solve multidigit addition problems. [Operations and Computation Goal 2]	1a. Solve a multidigit number story. [Operations and Computation Goal 2]	1b. Write a number model. [Patterns, Functions, and Algebra Goal 2]	2. Use data to make a bar graph. [Data and Chance Goal 1]	3. Find the rule for functions involving doubling. [Patterns, Functions, and Algebra Goal 1]	4–6. Identify 3-dimensional shapes. [Geometry Goal 2]	7. Solve multidigit addition problems with 3 or more addends. [Operations and Computation Goal 2]	8. Solve "What's My Rule?" with halving. [Patterns, Functions, and Algebra Goal 1]	9, 10. Order numbers and find median and mode. [Data and Chance Goal 2]	11. Fill in missing numbers on a number grid. [Patterns, Functions, and Algebra Goal 1]
1.											
2.											
3.											
4.											
5.											
6.											
7.											
8.											
9.											
10.											
11.											
12.											
13.											
14.											
15.											
16.											
17.											
18.											
19.											
20.											
21.											
22.											
23.											
24.											
25.											

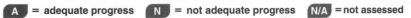

Assess Progress: **A** = adequate progress   **N** = not adequate progress   **N/A** = not assessed   **Formative Assessments**

Go to *www.everydaymathonline.com* for digital checklists.

Individual Profile of Progress

Name _____   Date _____

Lesson	Recognizing Student Achievement	A.P.*	Comments
8◆1	**Model fractions as equal parts of a region and name the fraction.** [Number and Numeration Goal 3]		
8◆2	**Record addition facts.** [Operations and Computation Goal 1]		
8◆3	**Calculate coin combinations.** [Operations and Computation Goal 2]		
8◆4	**Identify the value of digits in numbers.** [Number and Numeration Goal 2]		
8◆5	**Record equivalent fraction pairs.** [Number and Numeration Goal 6]		
8◆6	**Record equivalent units of time.** [Measurement and Reference Frames Goal 3]		
8◆7	**Solve fraction number stories involving fractions of a collection.** [Number and Numeration Goal 3]		

*Assess Progress: = adequate progress   = not adequate progress   = not assessed

Individual Profile of Progress

Name _____ Date _____

Problem(s)	Progress Check 8	A.P.*	Comments
Oral/Slate Assessment			
1–2	**Solve a word problem involving fractions.** [Number and Numeration Goal 3]		
3	**Write simple fractions.** [Number and Numeration Goal 3]		
4	**Divide slates into simple fractions as directed and answer questions.** [Number and Numeration Goal 3]		
Written Assessment Part A			
1–6	**Represent fractions as equal parts of a region or collection.** [Number and Numeration Goal 3]		
7, 8	**Use basic language of probability.** [Data and Chance Goal 3]		
9	**Identify objects that have a line of symmetry.** [Geometry Goal 3]		
Written Assessment Part B			
10, 11a, 12b, 13	**Represent fractions as equal parts of a region or collection.** [Number and Numeration Goal 3]		
11b	**Compare fractions.** [Number and Numeration Goal 7]		
11c	**Find equivalent names for common fractions.** [Number and Numeration Goal 6]		
12a	**Complete an equal-shares problem.** [Operations and Computation Goal 4]		

*Assess Progress: **A** = adequate progress   **N** = not adequate progress   **N/A** = not assessed   Formative Assessments

Class Checklist:
Recognizing Student Achievement

Class _____

Date _____

Names	8·1	8·2	8·3	8·4	8·5	8·6	8·7
	Model fractions as equal parts of a region and name the fraction. [Number and Numeration Goal 3]	**Record addition facts.** [Operations and Computation Goal 1]	**Calculate coin combinations.** [Operations and Computation Goal 2]	**Identify the value of digits in numbers.** [Number and Numeration Goal 2]	**Record equivalent fraction pairs.** [Number and Numeration Goal 6]	**Record equivalent units of time.** [Measurement and Reference Frames Goal 3]	**Solve fraction number stories involving fractions of a collection.** [Number and Numeration Goal 3]
1.							
2.							
3.							
4.							
5.							
6.							
7.							
8.							
9.							
10.							
11.							
12.							
13.							
14.							
15.							
16.							
17.							
18.							
19.							
20.							
21.							
22.							
23.							
24.							
25.							

Assess Progress: **A** = adequate progress **N** = not adequate progress **N/A** = not assessed

Class Checklist:

Progress Check 8

Class _____

Date _____

Names	Oral/Slate			Written Part A			Written Part B			
	1–2. Solve a word problem involving fractions. [Number and Numeration Goal 3]	3. Write simple fractions. [Number and Numeration Goal 3]	4. Divide slates into simple fractions as directed and answer questions. [Number and Numeration Goal 3]	1–6. Represent fractions as equal parts of a region or collection. [Number and Numeration Goal 3]	7, 8. Use basic language of probability. [Data and Chance Goal 3]	9. Identify objects that have a line of symmetry. [Geometry Goal 3]	10, 11a, 12b, 13. Represent fractions as equal parts of a region or collection. [Number and Numeration Goal 3]	11b. Compare fractions. [Number and Numeration Goal 7]	11c. Find equivalent names for common fractions. [Number and Numeration Goal 6]	12a. Complete an equal-shares problem. [Operations and Computation Goal 4]
1.										
2.										
3.										
4.										
5.										
6.										
7.										
8.										
9.										
10.										
11.										
12.										
13.										
14.										
15.										
16.										
17.										
18.										
19.										
20.										
21.										
22.										
23.										
24.										
25.										

Assess Progress: = adequate progress = not adequate progress **N/A** = not assessed **Formative Assessments**

Individual Profile of Progress

Name _____   Date _____

Lesson	Recognizing Student Achievement	A.P.*	Comments
9◆1	**Find the modes for data sets.** [Data and Chance Goal 2]		
9◆2	**Use a ruler to measure the lengths of objects.** [Measurement and Reference Frames Goal 1]		
9◆3	**Measure to the nearest inch.** [Measurement and Reference Frames Goal 1]		
9◆4	**Measure the sides of a rectangle to the nearest inch.** [Measurement and Reference Frames Goal 1]		
9◆5	**Find a fraction of a collection.** [Number and Numeration Goal 3]		
9◆6	**Record addition and subtraction facts.** [Operations and Computation Goal 1]		
9◆7	**Share counters equally.** [Operations and Computation Goal 4]		
9◆8	**Continue numeric patterns.** [Patterns, Functions, and Algebra Goal 1]		
9◆9	**Write number sentences and generate equivalent names for numbers.** [Number and Numeration Goal 5]		

*Assess Progress: = adequate progress   = not adequate progress   = not assessed

Individual Profile of Progress

Name _____   Date _____

Problem(s)	Progress Check 9	A.P.*	Comments
Oral/Slate Assessment			
1–3	**Use manipulatives to model an equivalent fraction in a word problem and describe strategies used.** [Number and Numeration Goal 6]		
4	**Make a ballpark estimate, with a number model, for each given sum.** [Operations and Computation Goal 3]		
5	**Solve addition problems of 2-digit whole numbers using strategies or manipulatives.** [Operations and Computation Goal 2]		
Written Assessment Part A			
1, 2	**Measure to the nearest inch and centimeter.** [Measurement and Reference Frames Goal 1]		
3, 4	**Partition rectangles and count unit squares to find areas.** [Measurement and Reference Frames Goal 2]		
5	**Draw a line segment.** [Geometry Goal 1]		
6	**Make a ballpark estimate and write a number model.** [Operations and Computation Goal 3]		
7, 8	**Find the median.** [Data and Chance Goal 2]		
9–12	**Add and subtract multidigit numbers.** [Operations and Computation Goal 2]		
Written Assessment Part B			
13	**Measure to the nearest half-centimeter.** [Measurement and Reference Frames Goal 1]		
14	**Find an equivalent name for $\frac{1}{2}$.** [Number and Numeration Goal 6]		
15	**Draw a parallel line segment and label its endpoints.** [Geometry Goal 1]		

*Assess Progress: **A** = adequate progress   **N** = not adequate progress   **N/A** = not assessed   **Formative Assessments**

Class Checklist:
Recognizing Student Achievement

Class _____

Date _____

Names	Find the modes for data sets. [Data and Chance Goal 2] 9·1	Use a ruler to measure the length of objects. [Measurement and Reference Frames Goal 1] 9·2	Measure to the nearest inch. [Measurement and Reference Frames Goal 1] 9·3	Measure the sides of a rectangle to the nearest inch. [Measurement and Reference Frames Goal 1] 9·4	Find a fraction of a collection. [Number and Numeration Goal 3] 9·5	Record addition and subtraction facts. [Operations and Computation Goal 1] 9·6	Share counters equally. [Operations and Computation Goal 4] 9·7	Continue numerical patterns. [Patterns, Functions, and Algebra Goal 1] 9·8	Write number sentences and generate equivalent names for numbers. [Number and Numeration Goal 5] 9·9
1.									
2.									
3.									
4.									
5.									
6.									
7.									
8.									
9.									
10.									
11.									
12.									
13.									
14.									
15.									
16.									
17.									
18.									
19.									
20.									
21.									
22.									
23.									
24.									
25.									

Assess Progress: **A** = adequate progress   **N** = not adequate progress   **N/A** = not assessed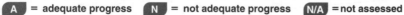

Class Checklist:
Progress Check 9

		Written		
	Oral/Slate	**Part A**		**Part B**

Names	1–3. Use manipulatives to model an equivalent fraction in a word problem. [Number and Numeration Goal 6]	4. Make a ballpark estimate, with a number model, for each given sum. [Operations and Computation Goal 3]	5. Solve addition problems of 2-digit whole numbers using strategies or manipulatives. [Operations and Computation Goal 2]	1, 2. Measure to the nearest inch and centimeter. [Measurement and Reference Frames Goal 1]	3, 4. Partition rectangles and count unit squares to find areas. [Measurement and Reference Frames Goal 2]	5. Draw a line segment. [Geometry Goal 1]	6. Make a ballpark estimate and write a number model. [Operations and Computation Goal 3]	7, 8. Find the median. [Data and Chance Goal 2]	9–12. Add and subtract multidigit numbers. [Operations and Computation Goal 2]	13. Measure to the nearest half-centimeter. [Measurement and Reference Frames Goal 1]	14. Find an equivalent name for $\frac{1}{2}$. [Number and Numeration Goal 6]	15. Draw a parallel line segment and label its endpoints. [Geometry Goal 1]
1.												
2.												
3.												
4.												
5.												
6.												
7.												
8.												
9.												
10.												
11.												
12.												
13.												
14.												
15.												
16.												
17.												
18.												
19.												
20.												
21.												
22.												
23.												
24.												
25.												

Class _____

Date _____

Assess Progress: **A** = adequate progress **N** = not adequate progress **N/A** = not assessed **Formative Assessments**

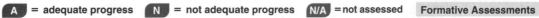

Individual Profile of Progress

Name _____   Date _____

Lesson	Recognizing Student Achievement	A.P.*	Comments
10◆1	**Calculate coin and bill combinations.** [Operations and Computation Goal 2]		
10◆2	**Estimate the combined values of two items.** [Operations and Computation Goal 3]		
10◆3	**Model fractions as equal parts of a collection.** [Number and Numeration Goal 3]		
10◆4	**Calculate coin and bill combinations.** [Operations and Computation Goal 2]		
10◆5	**Identify a rule for a function.** [Patterns, Functions, and Algebra Goal 1]		
10◆6	**Read the temperature.** [Measurement and Reference Frames Goal 5]		
10◆7	**Record addition facts.** [Operations and Computation Goal 1]		
10◆8	**Estimate the amount of change from a transaction.** [Operations and Computation Goal 3]		
10◆9	**Convert between units of time.** [Measurement and Reference Frames Goal 3]		
10◆10	**Identify the value of digits.** [Number and Numeration Goal 2]		
10◆11	**Identify fractions of a collection.** [Number and Numeration Goal 3]		

*Assess Progress: **A** = adequate progress **N** = not adequate progress **N/A** = not assessed

Individual Profile of Progress

Name _____ Date _____

Problem(s)	Progress Check 10	A.P.*	Comments
Oral/Slate Assessment			
1	**Identify the values of a 4-digit number.** [Number and Numeration Goal 2]		
2	**Read aloud money amounts written in dollars-and-cents notation.** [Number and Numeration Goal 2]		
3	**Write a 5-digit number and identify the place values.** [Number and Numeration Goal 2]		
4	**Write money amounts in dollars-and-cents notation.** [Number and Numeration Goal 2]		
Written Assessment Part A			
1	**Draw the lines of symmetry.** [Geometry Goal 3]		
2	**Count forward by 1s in thousands.** [Number and Numeration Goal 1]		
3, 4	**Read and write the temperature.** [Measurement and Reference Frames Goal 5]		
5	**Find the rule and complete the "What's My Rule?" table.** [Patterns, Functions, and Algebra Goal 1]		
6, 7	**Calculate the value of coin and bill combinations.** [Operations and Computation Goal 2]		
8, 9, 10	**Identify the value of digits in a number.** [Number and Numeration Goal 2]		
Written Assessment Part B			
11a	**Estimate total cost.** [Operations and Computation Goal 3]		
11b	**Write exact cost in dollars-and-cents notation.** [Number and Numeration Goal 2]		
12	**Find the correct amount of change.** [Operations and Computation Goal 2]		
13	**Solve an equal-shares problem.** [Operations and Computation Goal 4]		

*Assess Progress: **A** = adequate progress **N** = not adequate progress **N/A** = not assessed Formative Assessments

Class _____

Date _____

Names	Calculate coin and bill combinations. [Operations and Computation Goal 2] 10·1	Estimate the combined values of two items. [Operations and Computation Goal 3] 10·2	Model fractions as equal parts of a collection. [Number and Numeration Goal 3] 10·3	Calculate coin and bill combinations. [Operations and Computation Goal 2] 10·4	Identify a rule for a function. [Patterns, Functions, and Algebra Goal 1] 10·5	Read the temperature. [Measurement and Reference Frames 5] 10·6	Record addition facts. [Operations and Computation Goal 1] 10·7	Estimate the amount of change from a transaction. [Operations and Computation Goal 3] 10·8	Convert between units of time. [Measurement and Reference Frames Goal 3] 10·9	Identify the value of digits. [Number and Numeration Goal 2] 10·10	Identify fractions of a collection. [Number and Numeration Goal 3] 10·11
1.											
2.											
3.											
4.											
5.											
6.											
7.											
8.											
9.											
10.											
11.											
12.											
13.											
14.											
15.											
16.											
17.											
18.											
19.											
20.											
21.											
22.											
23.											
24.											
25.											

Assess Progress: **A** = adequate progress   **N** = not adequate progress   **N/A** = not assessed

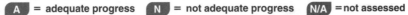

Go to *www.everydaymathonline.com* for digital checklists.

Class _____

Date _____

Names	Oral/Slate				Written Part A						Part B			
	1. Identify the values of a 4-digit number. [Number and Numeration Goal 2]	2. Read aloud money amounts in dollars-and-cents notation. [Number and Numeration Goal 2]	3. Write a 5-digit number and identify the place values. [Number and Numeration Goal 2]	4. Write money amounts in dollars-and-cents notation. [Number and Numeration Goal 2]	1. Draw the lines of symmetry. [Geometry Goal 3]	2. Count forward by 1s in thousands. [Number and Numeration Goal 1]	3, 4. Read and write the temperature. [Measurement and Reference Frames Goal 5]	5. Find the rule and complete the "What's My Rule?" table. [Patterns, Functions, and Algebra Goal 1]	6, 7. Calculate the value of coin and bill combinations. [Operations and Computation Goal 2]	8, 9, 10. Identify the value of digits in a number. [Number and Numeration Goal 2]	11a. Estimate total cost. [Operations and Computation Goal 3]	11b. Write exact cost in dollars-and-cents notation. [Number and Numeration Goal 2]	12. Find the correct amount of change. [Operations and Computation Goal 2]	13. Solve an equal-shares problem. [Operations and Computation Goal 4]
1.														
2.														
3.														
4.														
5.														
6.														
7.														
8.														
9.														
10.														
11.														
12.														
13.														
14.														
15.														
16.														
17.														
18.														
19.														
20.														
21.														
22.														
23.														
24.														
25.														

Assess Progress:  **A** = adequate progress **N** = not adequate progress **N/A** = not assessed **Formative Assessments**

Individual Profile of Progress

Name _____   Date _____

Lesson	Recognizing Student Achievement	A.P.*	Comments
11◆1	**Find differences between multidigit numbers.** [Operations and Computation Goal 2]		
11◆2	**Tell time to the nearest 5 minutes.** [Measurement and Reference Frames Goal 6]		
11◆3	**Solve multidigit subtraction problems.** [Operations and Computation Goal 2]		
11◆4	**Solve a multiplication problem using an equal groups model.** [Operations and Computation Goal 4]		
11◆5	**Solve a division problem using an equal sharing model.** [Operations and Computation Goal 4]		
11◆6	**Draw arrays for multiplication facts.** [Operations and Computation Goal 4]		
11◆7	**Draw sides of a rectangle to the nearest inch.** [Measurement and Reference Frames Goal 1]		
11◆8	**Find the median of a set of data.** [Data and Chance Goal 2]		
11◆9	**Estimate to solve addition problems with money.** [Operations and Computation Goal 3]		

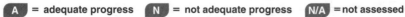
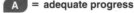

*Assess Progress: **A** = adequate progress   **N** = not adequate progress   **N/A** = not assessed

Go to *www.everydaymathonline.com* for digital checklists.

Individual Profile of Progress

Name _____ Date _____

Problem(s)	Progress Check 11	A.P.*	Comments
Oral/Slate Assessment			
1	**Make a reasonable estimate involving money in an addition word problem.** [Operations and Computation Goal 3]		
2	**Make a reasonable estimate involving money in a subtraction word problem.** [Operations and Computation Goal 3]		
3	**Solve a number story involving multiples of equal groups.** [Operations and Computation Goal 4]		
4	**Solve a number story involving equal sharing and equal grouping.** [Operations and Computation Goal 4]		
Written Assessment Part A			
1, 2	**Make change.** [Operations and Computation Goal 2]		
3	**Find equal shares.** [Operations and Computation Goal 4]		
4–6	**Draw arrays to model multiplication.** [Operations and Computation Goal 4]		
7–10	**Compare fractions.** [Number and Numeration Goal 7]		
11–14	**Solve addition and subtraction problems.** [Operations and Computation Goal 2]		
Written Assessment Part B			
15, 16	**Add and subtract dollars and cents.** [Operations and Computation Goal 2]		
17	**Solve a multiplication number story.** [Operations and Computation Goal 4]		
18	**Solve a division number story.** [Operations and Computation Goal 4]		

*Assess Progress: **A** = adequate progress   **N** = not adequate progress   **N/A** = not assessed   **Formative Assessments**

Class Checklist:
Recognizing Student Achievement

Class _____

Date _____

Names	11·1 Find differences between multidigit numbers. [Operations and Computation Goal 2]	11·2 Tell time to the nearest 5 minutes. [Measurement and Reference Frames Goal 6]	11·3 Solve multidigit subtraction problems. [Operations and Computation Goal 2]	11·4 Solve a multiplication problem using an equal groups model. [Operations and Computation Goal 4]	11·5 Solve a division problem using an equal sharing model. [Operations and Computation Goal 4]	11·6 Draw arrays for multiplication facts. [Operations and Computation Goal 4]	11·7 Draw sides of a rectangle to the nearest inch. [Measurement and Reference Frames Goal 1]	11·8 Find the median of a set of data. [Data and Chance Goal 2]	11·9 Estimate to solve addition problems with money. [Operations and Computation Goal 3]
1.									
2.									
3.									
4.									
5.									
6.									
7.									
8.									
9.									
10.									
11.									
12.									
13.									
14.									
15.									
16.									
17.									
18.									
19.									
20.									
21.									
22.									
23.									
24.									
25.									

Assess Progress: **A** = adequate progress   **N** = not adequate progress   **N/A** = not assessed

Go to *www.everydaymathonline.com* for digital checklists.

Class _____

Date _____

Names	Oral/Slate				Written Part A					Written Part B		
	1. Make a reasonable estimate involving money in an addition word problem. [Operations and Computation Goal 3]	2. Make a reasonable estimate involving money in a subtraction word problem. [Operations and Computation Goal 3]	3. Solve a number story involving multiples of equal groups. [Operations and Computation Goal 4]	4. Solve a number story involving equal sharing and equal grouping. [Operations and Computation Goal 4]	1, 2. Make change. [Operations and Computation Goal 2]	3. Find equal shares. [Operations and Computation Goal 4]	4–6. Draw arrays to model multiplication. [Operations and Computation Goal 4]	7–10. Compare fractions. [Number and Numeration Goal 7]	11–14. Solve addition and subtraction problems. [Operation and Computation Goal 2]	15, 16. Add and subtract dollars and cents. [Operations and Computation Goal 2]	17. Solve a multiplication number story. [Operations and Computation Goal 4]	18. Solve a division number story. [Operations and Computation Goal 4]
1.												
2.												
3.												
4.												
5.												
6.												
7.												
8.												
9.												
10.												
11.												
12.												
13.												
14.												
15.												
16.												
17.												
18.												
19.												
20.												
21.												
22.												
23.												
24.												
25.												

Assess Progress: **A** = adequate progress **N** = not adequate progress **N/A** = not assessed **Formative Assessments**

Individual Profile of Progress

Name _____ Date _____

Lesson	Recognizing Student Achievement	A.P.*	Comments
12◆1	**Describe the relationship between days in one week and hours in one day.** [Measurement and Reference Frames Goal 3]		
12◆2	**Record addition and subtraction facts.** [Operations and Computation Goal 1]		
12◆3	**Identify units of time.** [Measurement and Reference Frames Goal 3]		
12◆4	**Solve problems involving multiplication.** [Operations and Computation Goal 4]		
12◆5	**Use arrays to model multiplication facts.** [Operations and Computation Goal 4]		
12◆6	**Read a bar graph.** [Data and Chance Goal 2]		
12◆7	**Find landmarks of a data set.** [Data and Chance Goal 2]		

*Assess Progress: 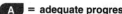 **A** = adequate progress **N** = not adequate progress **N/A** = not assessed

Individual Profile of Progress

_____   _____
Name   Date

Problem(s)	Progress Check 12	A.P.*	Comments
Oral/Slate Assessment			
1	**Name the days of the week.** [Measurement and Reference Frames Goal 3]		
2	**Name the months of the year.** [Measurement and Reference Frames Goal 3]		
3–4	**Solve a word problem involving multiplication.** [Operations and Computation Goal 4]		
Written Assessment Part A			
1–6	**Use graphs to find the maximum, minimum, mode, and median of a data set and determine who ran more and who ran fewer miles.** [Data and Chance Goal 2]		
7	**Make change.** [Operations and Computation Goal 2]		
8–11	**Find equivalent units of time.** [Measurement and Reference Frames Goal 3]		
12	**Shade regions and write fractions equivalent to $\frac{1}{2}$.** [Number and Numeration Goal 6]		
13	**Compare and order large numbers.** [Number and Numeration Goal 7]		
Written Assessment Part B			
14–20	**Write the fact family for a Fact Triangle. Solve multiplication fact problems.** [Operations and Computation Goal 4]		
21, 22	**Draw hour and minute hands to show times.** [Measurement and Reference Frames Goal 6]		

*Assess Progress: **A** = adequate progress   **N** = not adequate progress   **N/A** = not assessed   Formative Assessments

Class Checklist:
Recognizing Student Achievement

Class _____

Date _____

Names	Describe the relationship between days in one week and hours in one day. [Measurement and Reference Frames Goal 3] 12·1	Record addition and subtraction facts. [Operations and Computation Goal 1] 12·2	Identify units of time. [Measurement and Reference Frames Goal 3] 12·3	Solve problems involving multiplication. [Operations and Computation Goal 4] 12·4	Draw arrays to model multiplication facts. [Operations and Computation Goal 4] 12·5	Read a bar graph. [Data and Chance Goal 2] 12·6	Find landmarks of a data set. [Data and Chance Goal 2] 12·7
1.							
2.							
3.							
4.							
5.							
6.							
7.							
8.							
9.							
10.							
11.							
12.							
13.							
14.							
15.							
16.							
17.							
18.							
19.							
20.							
21.							
22.							
23.							
24.							
25.							

Assess Progress: **A** = adequate progress   **N** = not adequate progress   **N/A** = not assessed

Go to *www.everydaymathonline.com* for digital checklists.

Class Checklist:
Progress Check 12

Class _____

Date _____

Names	Oral/Slate			Written Part A						Part B	
	1. Name the days of the week. [Measurement and Reference Frames Goal 3]	2. Name the months of the year. [Measurement and Reference Frames Goal 3]	3–4. Solve a word problem involving multiplication. [Operations and Computation Goal 4]	1–6. Use graphs to find the maximum, minimum, mode, and median of a data set and determine who ran more and who ran fewer miles. [Data and Chance Goal 2]	7. Make change. [Operations and Computation Goal 2]	8–11. Find equivalent units of time. [Measurement and Reference Frames Goal 3]	12. Shade regions and write fractions equivalent to $\frac{1}{2}$. [Number and Numeration Goal 6]	13. Compare and order large numbers. [Number and Numeration Goal 7]	14–20. Write the fact family for a Fact Triangle. Solve multiplication fact problems. [Operations and Computation Goal 4]	21, 22. Draw hour and minute hands to show times. [Measurement and Reference Frames Goal 6]	
1.											
2.											
3.											
4.											
5.											
6.											
7.											
8.											
9.											
10.											
11.											
12.											
13.											
14.											
15.											
16.											
17.											
18.											
19.											
20.											
21.											
22.											
23.											
24.											
25.											

Assess Progress: 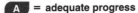 = adequate progress  = not adequate progress  = not assessed   **Formative Assessments**

Quarterly Checklist: Quarter 1

Names	Goal	7	5	7	4	1	5	5	2	5	2	2	1	2	1	2	4	1	1	1	2	2
	Lesson	1•1	1•9	1•11	1•12	2•3	2•9	3•1	3•3	3•5	3•7	1•2	1•4	1•5	1•6	1•10	2•1	2•2	2•4	2•5	2•12	3•2	3•8
	Date																						
		Number and Numeration										**Operations and Computation**											
1.																							
2.																							
3.																							
4.																							
5.																							
6.																							
7.																							
8.																							
9.																							
10.																							
11.																							
12.																							
13.																							
14.																							
15.																							
16.																							
17.																							
18.																							
19.																							
20.																							
21.																							
22.																							

Quarterly Checklist: Quarter 1

Names	Data and Chance				Measurement and Reference Frames		Geometry			Patterns, Functions, and Algebra								
Goal					6	6				1	1	3	2	1	1	2	2	1
Lesson					1·3	3·4				1·7	1·8	2·6	2·7	2·8	2·10	2·11	2·13	3·6
Date																		
1.																		
2.																		
3.																		
4.																		
5.																		
6.																		
7.																		
8.																		
9.																		
10.																		
11.																		
12.																		
13.																		
14.																		
15.																		
16.																		
17.																		
18.																		
19.																		
20.																		
21.																		
22.																		

Quarterly Checklist: Quarter 2

		Number and Numeration	Operations and Computation														
Goal		5	4	4	3	1	3	2	3	2	2	4	2	4	4	4
Lesson		4•3	4•1	4•2	4•5	4•7	4•8	4•9	5•5	5•6	6•1	6•2	6•4	6•7	6•8	6•10
Date																
Names																
1.																
2.																
3.																
4.																
5.																
6.																
7.																
8.																
9.																
10.																
11.																
12.																
13.																
14.																
15.																
16.																
17.																
18.																
19.																
20.																
21.																
22.																

Quarterly Checklist: Quarter 2

Names	Data and Chance		Measurements and Reference Frames					Geometry				Patterns, Functions, and Algebra
Goal	2	3	5	6	6	4	1	1	1	2	3	1
Lesson	6·3	6·5	4·4	4·6	5·1	6·6	6·9	5·2	5·3	5·4	5·8	5·7
Date												
1.												
2.												
3.												
4.												
5.												
6.												
7.												
8.												
9.												
10.												
11.												
12.												
13.												
14.												
15.												
16.												
17.												
18.												
19.												
20.												
21.												
22.												

Quarterly Checklist: Quarter 3

Names	Goal			Number and Numeration								Operations and Computation						
	Goal	1	3	2	6	3	3	5		2	2	4	1	2	1	4	
	Lesson	7·1	8·1	8·4	8·5	8·7	9·5	9·9		7·2	7·3	7·5	8·2	8·3	9·6	9·7	
	Date																
1.																	
2.																	
3.																	
4.																	
5.																	
6.																	
7.																	
8.																	
9.																	
10.																	
11.																	
12.																	
13.																	
14.																	
15.																	
16.																	
17.																	
18.																	
19.																	
20.																	
21.																	
22.																	

Quarterly Checklist: Quarter 3

Names	Data and Chance			Measurement and Reference Frames						Geometry		Patterns, Functions, and Algebra	
Goal	2	2		1	6	3	1	1	1			1	1
Lesson	7·8	9·1		7·6	7·7	8·6	9·2	9·3	9·4			7·4	9·8
Date													
1.													
2.													
3.													
4.													
5.													
6.													
7.													
8.													
9.													
10.													
11.													
12.													
13.													
14.													
15.													
16.													
17.													
18.													
19.													
20.													
21.													
22.													

Quarterly Checklist: Quarter 4

Names	Goal / Lesson / Date	Number and Numeration			Operations and Computation													
	Goal	3	2	3	2	3	2	1	3	2	2	4	4	4	3	1	4	4
	Lesson	10·3	10·10	10·11	10·1	10·2	10·4	10·7	10·8	11·1	11·3	11·4	11·5	11·6	11·9	12·2	12·4	12·5
	Date																	
1.																		
2.																		
3.																		
4.																		
5.																		
6.																		
7.																		
8.																		
9.																		
10.																		
11.																		
12.																		
13.																		
14.																		
15.																		
16.																		
17.																		
18.																		
19.																		
20.																		
21.																		
22.																		

Quarterly Checklist: Quarter 4

Names	Data and Chance			Measurement and Reference Frames							Geometry				Patterns, Functions, and Algebra			
Goal	2	2	2	5	3	6	1	3	3					1			
Lesson	11·8	12·6	12·7	10·6	10·9	11·2	11·7	12·1	12·3					10·5			
Date																	
1.																	
2.																	
3.																	
4.																	
5.																	
6.																	
7.																	
8.																	
9.																	
10.																	
11.																	
12.																	
13.																	
14.																	
15.																	
16.																	
17.																	
18.																	
19.																	
20.																	
21.																	
22.																	

Individual Profile of Progress

Name _____ Date _____

Lesson	Recognizing Student Achievement	A.P.*	Comments

*Assess Progress: **A** = adequate progress **N** = not adequate progress **N/A** = not assessed

Class Checklist:
Recognizing Student Achievement

Unit

Class _____

Date _____

Names							
1.							
2.							
3.							
4.							
5.							
6.							
7.							
8.							
9.							
10.							
11.							
12.							
13.							
14.							
15.							
16.							
17.							
18.							
19.							
20.							
21.							
22.							
23.							
24.							
25.							

Assess Progress:  **A** = adequate progress **N** = not adequate progress **N/A** = not assessed

Copyright © Wright Group/McGraw-Hill

Name _____ Date _____

Parent Reflections

Use some of the following questions (or your own) and tell us how you see your child progressing in mathematics.

Do you see evidence of your child using mathematics at home?

What do you think are your child's strengths and challenges in mathematics?

Does your child demonstrate responsibility for completing Home Links?

What thoughts do you have about your child's progress in mathematics?

Name   Date   Time

My Exit Slip

✂ -

Name   Date   Time

My Exit Slip

About My Math Class A

Draw a face or write the words
that show how you feel.

Good   OK   Not so good

1. This is how I feel about math:	**2.** This is how I feel about working with a partner or in a group:	**3.** This is how I feel about working by myself:
4. This is how I feel about solving number stories:	**5.** This is how I feel about doing Home Links with my family:	**6.** This is how I feel about finding new ways to solve problems:

Circle **yes, sometimes,** or **no.**

7. I like to figure things out. I am curious.

yes   sometimes   no

8. I keep trying even when I don't understand
something right away.

yes   sometimes   no

About My Math Class B

Circle the word that best describes how you feel.

1. I enjoy mathematics class. **yes** **sometimes** **no**

2. I like to work with a partner **yes** **sometimes** **no**
or in a group.

3. I like to work by myself. **yes** **sometimes** **no**

4. I like to solve problems **yes** **sometimes** **no**
in mathematics.

5. I enjoy doing Home Links **yes** **sometimes** **no**
with my family.

6. In mathematics, I am good at _____

_____

_____

7. One thing I like about mathematics is _____

_____

_____

8. One thing I find difficult in mathematics is _____

_____

_____

Math Log A

What did you learn in mathematics this week?

Math Log B

Question:

_____

- -

_____

_____

- -

_____

_____

- -

_____

_____

- -

_____

_____

- -

_____

_____

- -

_____

_____

- -

_____

_____

- -

_____

Math Log C

Work Box	Tell how you solved this problem.
	_____
	_____
	_____
	_____
	_____

300

✂

Math Log C

Work Box	Tell how you solved this problem.
	_____
	_____
	_____
	_____
	_____

Good Work!

I have chosen this work for my portfolio because

Name _____ Date _____ Time _____

My Work ✓

This work shows that I can _____

_____

_____

I am still learning to _____

_____

_____

_____

302

- ✂

Name _____ Date _____ Time _____

My Work ✓

This work shows that I can _____

_____

_____

I am still learning to _____

_____

_____

_____

Name-Collection Boxes

1.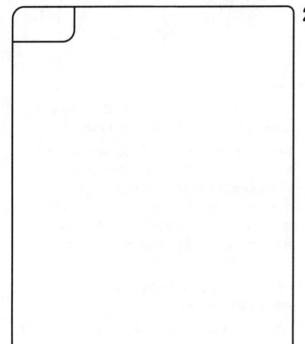

2.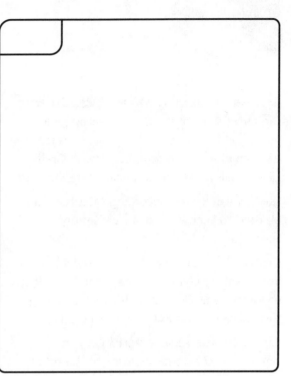

3.

4.

Glossary

Assessment Management Spreadsheets Digital versions of the Class Checklists and Individual Profiles of Progress that help teachers track child and class progress toward Grade-Level Goals and Common Core State Standards.

Class Checklists Recording tools that can be used to keep track of a class's progress on specific Grade-Level Goals.

Content for Assessment Material that is important for children to learn and is the focus of assessment. *Everyday Mathematics* highlights this content through Grade-Level Goals.

Contexts for Assessment Ongoing, periodic, and external assessments based on products or observations.

Enrichment Activities Optional activities that apply or deepen children's understanding.

Evidence from Assessment Information about children's knowledge, skills, and dispositions collected from observations or products.

External Assessments Assessments that are independent of the curriculum, for example, standardized tests.

Formative Assessments Assessments that provide information about children's current knowledge and abilities so that teachers can plan future instruction more effectively and so that children can identify their own areas of weakness or strength.

Grade-Level Goals Mathematical goals organized by content strand and articulated across grade levels from Pre-Kindergarten through Grade 6.

Individual Profile of Progress A recording tool that can be used to keep track of children's progress on specific Grade-Level Goals.

Informing Instruction These notes in the *Teacher's Lesson Guide* suggest how to use observations of children's work to adapt instruction by describing common errors and misconceptions in children's thinking and alerting the teacher to multiple solution strategies or unique insights children might offer.

Making Adequate Progress On a trajectory to meet a Grade-Level Goal.

Math Boxes Collections of problems designed to provide distributed practice. Math Boxes revisit content from prior units to build and maintain important concepts and skills. One or two problems on each page preview content from the next unit.

Mental Math and Reflexes Exercises at three levels of difficulty that prepare children for the lesson, build mental-arithmetic skills, and help teachers quickly assess individual strengths and weaknesses.

Observational Assessments Assessments based on observing children during daily activities or periodic assessments.

Ongoing Assessments Assessments based on children's everyday work during regular classroom instruction.

Open Response An extended response assessment included in the Progress Check lesson of each unit.

Periodic Assessments Formal assessments that are built into a curriculum such as the end-of-unit Progress Checks.

Portfolios Collections of student products and observations that provide opportunities for children to reflect on their mathematical growth and for teachers to understand and document that growth.

Product Assessments Assessments based on children's work from daily activities or from periodic assessments.

Program Evaluation Assessment intended to reveal how well a program of instruction is working. A school district, for example, might carry out program evaluation to identify schools with strong mathematics programs so that their success can be replicated.

Program Goals The fifteen cross-grade goals in *Everyday Mathematics* that weave the program together across grade levels. They form an organizing framework that supports both curriculum and assessment. Every Grade-Level Goal is linked to a Program Goal.

Progress Check The last lesson in every unit. Progress Check lessons include a student Self Assessment, an Oral and Slate Assessment, a Written Assessment, and an Open Response task.

Purposes of Assessment The reasons for assessment, which include providing information that can be used to plan future instruction, identifying what students have achieved during a period of time, and evaluating the quality of the mathematics program.

Readiness Activities Optional activities in many lessons that preview lesson content or provide alternative routes of access for learning concepts and skills.

Recognizing Student Achievement A feature in many lessons that highlights specific tasks used to monitor children's progress toward Grade-Level Goals. The notes identify the expectations for a child who is making adequate progress and point to skills or strategies that some children might be able to demonstrate.

Rubric A set of suggested guidelines for scoring assessment activities.

Student Self Assessment The individual reflection included in the Progress Check lesson of each unit.

Summative Assessments Assessments that aim to measure children's growth and achievement, for example, an assessment to determine whether children have learned certain material by the end of a fixed period of study such as a semester or a course.

Writing/Reasoning Prompt A question linked to a specific Math Boxes problem. Writing/Reasoning Prompts provide children with opportunities to respond to questions that extend and deepen their mathematical thinking.

Written Progress Check The Written Assessment included in the Progress Check Lesson of each unit.

Index